UNITS
OF MEASUREMENT
OF PHYSICAL QUANTITIES

UNITS
OF MEASUREMENT
OF PHYSICAL QUANTITIES

A. G. CHERTOV

Translated by Scripta Technica, Inc.
English-language edition revised and augmented by
Herbert J. Eagle
Brown University

HAYDEN BOOK COMPANY, INC., NEW YORK
a division of HAYDEN PUBLISHING COMPANY, INC.

Copyright © 1964

HAYDEN BOOK COMPANY, INC.

Library of Congress Catalog Card Number 64-24370

Printed in the United States of America

PREFACE

Among the thousands of technical books published in the Soviet Union each year there appears—although very seldom—a volume that is unmistakably and definitely a rare "find." We at Scripta Technica believe, indeed we know, that the present work by Professor Chertov is such a find. The first edition of UNITS OF MEASUREMENT OF PHYSICAL QUANTITIES was published in Moscow in 1958. This edition was sold out in less than one year, and a second, revised and updated edition of 25,000 was put on the market less than two years later to satisfy the demand. It is, of course, impossible to compare the number of copies sold in the Soviet Union with the needs of the Western scientific community. Nevertheless, these numbers are impressive and should, to a certain extent, provide an index of this book's value in the English-speaking world.

UNITS OF MEASUREMENT OF PHYSICAL QUANTITIES is a unique and convenient volume that will be of equal interest as a textbook to the advanced high school student and graduate physics or engineering major, or as a reference volume to the teacher as well as the practicing physicist, chemist, engineer, or laboratory and industrial technician. The coverage combines treatment of units, dimensional analysis, and good physics and provides a fundamental contribution to the subject. The author takes nothing for granted; every step is explicitly explained by proof and derivation. Although the subject of units of physical quantities is usually touched upon in fundamental textbooks on physics, chemistry, or engineering, and while most handbooks contain a small section devoted to this topic accompanied by a number of numerical conversion tables, no work equivalent to this one exists in the English language.

We are indebted to Herbert Eagle of Brown University, now serving with the Peace Corps somewhere in India, who edited and extended each and every section of this book to include, keeping Prof. Chertov's original approach, the treatment of the British

v

system of units, such as the foot, the pound, the BTU, etc. A number of sections dealing with units applicable only to the Soviet Union and deemed superfluous for this volume were likewise eliminated.

The reader should note that this text uses the following designations for the fps system: the abbreviation $f\ lbm\ s$ is used to denote the absolute system's pound mass and $f\ lbf\ s$ is used to denote the gravitational system's pound force.

September, 1964   William Begell
NEW YORK, N. Y.   SCRIPTA TECHNICA, INC.

CONTENTS

Preface v

Greek Alphabet ix

Chapter I. General Aspects of Selection of Units. Formulation
of Systems of Units 1
   1. Selection of Units of Measurement. Fundamental and
Derived Quantities and Units 3
   2. Dimensions of Derived Quantities and Units of Measurement 6
   3. Proportionality Factor in Physical Formulas 9
      1. Proportionality Factor in Fundamental Equations . . 9
      2. Proportionality Factor in Physical Formulas Which
Are Not Fundamental Equations 10
   4. Systems of Units Adopted in Science and Engineering . . 11

Chapter II. Systems of Mechanical Units 13
   1. The MKS System (practical) 13
      1. Fundamental Units in the MKS System 13
      2. Derived Units in the MKS System 14
   2. The cgs System (physical) 22
      1. Fundamental Units in the cgs System 22
      2. Derived Units in the cgs System 23
   3. The Metric Gravitational (MKGFS) System (Technical) . 24
      1. Fundamental Units in the MKGFS System 24
      2. Derived Units in the MKGFS System 24
   4. The British Absolute (f lbm s) System 30
      1. Fundamental Units in the f lbm s System 31
      2. Derived Units in the f lbm s System 31
   5. The British Gravitational (f lbf s) System 38
      1. Fundamental Units in the f lbf s System 39
      2. Derived Units in the f lbf s System 39
   6. Relationships Among Mechanical Units in Different
Systems 44
      1. Relationship Among Units in MKS and cgs Systems . 45
      2. Relationships Among Units in the MKS and f lbm s
Systems 49
      3. Other Units in the f lbm s and f lbf s Systems 53

    4. Relationships Among Units in the f lbm s and f lbf s
      Systems 54
  7. Other Units of Mechanical Quantities 55
  8. Rules for Calculation in Solving Physical Problems .. 59

Chapter III. Units of Measurement of Acoustic Quantities ... 64
  1. Units of Measurement of Quantities Characterising Sound
    as a Physical Phenomenon 64
  2. Units of Measurement of Quantities Characterising Sound
    as a Psycho-Physical Phenomenon 68

Chapter IV. Units of Measurement of Quantities Used in Molec-
    ular Physics 72
  1. Temperature 73
  2. Derived Molecular Physics Units in the MKS and cgs
    Systems.................................... 76
  3. Solution of Problems in Molecular Physics 84

Chapter V. Systems of Units for Measurement of Electromag-
    netic Quantities 87
  1. The MKSA (practical) System 87
  2. The cgs esu System.......................... 102
  3. The cgs emu System 109
  4. The cgs System (Gaussian System) 117
  5. The Rationalized MKSAr system 119
  6. Relationships Among Electromagnetic Units in Different
    Systems 122
  7. Sample Solutions of Problems in Electromagnetism .. 129

Chapter VI. Units of Measurement of Quantities of Electro-
    magnetic Radiation 133
  1. Units of Measurement of Energy Quantities in Electro-
    magnetic Radiation 134
  2. Units of Measurement of Quantities of Thermal Radiation 137
  3. Units of Measurement of Photometric Quantities 138
  4. Units of Measurement of Quantities of Radioactive Decay 141
  5. Units of Measurement of Quantities Characterizing the
    Action Between Radiation and Matter 143

Appendices 151
Index 163

GREEK ALPHABET

A	α — Alpha		N	ν — Nu
B	β — Beta		Ξ	ξ — Xi
Γ	γ — Gamma		O	o — Omicron
Δ	δ — Delta		Π	π — Pi
E	ϵ — Epsilon		P	ρ — Rho
Z	ζ — Zeta		Σ	σ — Sigma
H	η — Eta		T	τ — Tau
Θ	θ — Theta		Υ	υ — Upsilon
I	ι — Iota		Φ	φ — Phi
K	κ — Kappa		X	χ — Chi
Λ	λ — Lambda		Ψ	ψ — Psi
M	μ — Mu		Ω	ω — Omega

Chapter I

GENERAL ASPECTS OF SELECTION OF UNITS. FORMULATION OF SYSTEMS OF UNITS

The study of the laws governing physical phenomena and the application of these laws in engineering involve the measurement of physical quantities.

Measuring a quantity means comparing it with a standard quantity of the same nature. This standard quantity is known as a unit of measurement. The unit (for a given physical quantity) is selected in such a way as to be convenient for the measurement of those magnitudes of the quantity that are most frequently encountered in practice. For example, the meter (in the metric system) and the foot (in the British system*) have been chosen as fundamental units for the measurement of length.

The meter (or the foot) is conveniently used to measure the dimensions of apartment houses, industrial plants, small plots of land, the span of bridges, the height of trees, etc.

However, the meter is unsuitable for many measurements; it is too small, for example, to measure conveniently the distance between towns or the distance between heavenly bodies, while it is far too large to measure the dimensions of the elementary particles which form the atom and the atomic nucleus, or to measure the wavelength of light. Thus, the meter (or the foot) must be transformed into multiple or fractional (submultiple) units of length.

Multiple units are derived from the fundamental unit by multiplication by an integer. The kilometer (km) = 1000 meters and the mile = 5280 feet are examples of multiple units of length.

Submultiple units are derived from the fundamental unit by division by an integer. The following are submultiple units:

---

*Although the foot is the fundamental unit in the British system, it is actually the yard which is maintained in London, with a copy in the National Bureau of Standards in Washington.

Metric System

1 centimeter = 0.01 meter
1 millimeter = 0.001 meter
1 micron   = 10^{-6} meter
1 millimicron = 10^{-9} meter, etc.

British System

1 inch = 1/12 foot

Fundamental units for other quantities, like the fundamental units of length (the meter or the foot), are selected on the basis of their suitability for measuring the magnitudes most frequently encountered in practice. Thus, we have the following fundamental units: kilogram (or pound) for measuring *mass*; day for measuring *time*; ampere for measuring *current*, etc. A large number of convenient multiple and submultiple units can be formed from these fundamental units. In forming multiple and submultiple units, prefixes are often added to the basic unit of the physical quantity. For example, milliliter (10^{-3} liter), picofarad (10^{-12} farad), megohm (10^{6} ohm), etc.

Here is a list of the prefixes used to form multiple and submultiple units.

Prefixes for multiple units	Relationship to fundamental unit	Symbol	Prefixes for submultiple units	Relationship to fundamental unit	Symbol
Tera	10^{12}	T	Deci	10^{-1}	d
Giga	10^{9}	G	Centi	10^{-2}	c
Mega	10^{6}	M	Milli	10^{-3}	m
Kilo	10^{3}	k	Micro	10^{-6}	μ
Hecto	10^{2}	h	Nano	10^{-9}	n
Deca	10	dc	Pico	10^{-12}	p

The fundamental unit for a physical quantity had to be selected in such a way that it could be reproduced in case of loss. For example, the meter was originally chosen as one 40-millionth of the meridian through Paris; the kilogram was chosen as the mass of one cubic decimeter of distilled water at 4°C. To preserve these units of measurement, standards were manufactured, and these standards are now kept in the International Weights and Measures Office in Paris. Copies of these standards are kept in the Bureaus of Standards of different countries and are employed to determine and check the units of measurement presently in use.

Since it is not possible to reproduce a unit of measurement with absolute accuracy, it has been universally agreed to consider the standard, rather than the original prototype, as the basis of the unit of measurement. Thus, a meter is not one 40-millionth of the meridian through Paris, but the length of the standard originally manufactured on the basis of a measurement of this meridian (the exact definition of a meter is given below).

The units of length, mass, time, and current mentioned above were chosen arbitrarily. Their selection was dictated by convenience of application in practice. However, as will become clear from the following considerations, the units of many physical quantities are not chosen arbitrarily, but are derived on the basis of natural relationships existing between physical quantities. In some cases, the magnitudes of the units thus derived are unsuitable for practical use. Such units are, nevertheless, retained, in order to preserve the completeness of certain groups of units derived from physical laws. These groups are termed *systems of units*.

Both individual units and systems of units have been altered or replaced in the course of time to keep pace with the requirements of science and engineering. In order to be able to use units of measurement intelligently when solving physical problems, or when considering practical questions, we have to understand the variety of the existing units, and be able to answer the questions: How were the different units selected? What is the relationship between them? How can we express one unit in terms of another? etc.

1. SELECTION OF UNITS OF MEASUREMENT.

Fundamental and Derived Quantities
and Units

Let us first consider the selection of units. Let us assume that we have chosen the meter as a unit of length. Independently of this choice, we can also arbitrarily select a unit of time and a unit of mass, since length, time, and mass, as individual quantities, are not interrelated among each other in any way. Let us choose the second as the unit of time, and the kilogram as the unit of mass. (We could have also begun by choosing the second as the unit of time, the foot as the unit of length, and the pound as the unit of mass.) Having already selected units of time and length, if we arbitrarily choose a unit of velocity as well, we will create unnecessary complications in the use of the equation for velocity.

The velocity v, the distance traveled (displacement) s, and the time interval t in which the displacement occurs are related by the well-known equation:

$$v = k \frac{s}{t} \qquad (1.1)$$

where k is a proportionality (or conversion) factor.

We can assume that in Eq. (1.1) $k = 1$. The equation is then simplified and takes the form:

$$v = \frac{s}{t}; \tag{1.2}$$

However, we can easily note that this equation also determines the unit of velocity as 1 m/sec (one meter per second), since we have selected 1 meter as the unit of distance and 1 second as the unit of time.

If, on the other hand, the unit of velocity is chosen at random, for example, as 1 km/hr (one kilometer per hour), the factor k in Eq. (1.1) will no longer be equal to unity. Its value, according to this equation, is determined from the relationship:

$$\text{km/hr} = k.(\text{m/sec})$$

whence:

$$k = \frac{\text{km/hr}}{\text{m/sec}} = \frac{\text{km . sec}}{\text{m . hr}} = \frac{(1000 \text{ m}). \text{ sec}}{\text{m.}(3600 \text{ sec})} = \frac{5}{18}$$

Thus, if we express the length in meters, the time in seconds, and the velocity in kilometers per hour, the proportionality factor in Eq. (1.1) will be equal to 5/18, and the velocity equation will become:

$$v = \frac{5}{18} \cdot \frac{s}{t} \tag{1.3}$$

Comparison of Eqs. (1.2) and (1.3) shows that the arbitrary selection of the units of velocity has greatly complicated the equation and made it rather cumbersome. This means that it is not advisable to select the units for velocity arbitrarily. This unit should be selected on the basis of the velocity equation with the proportionality factor k set equal to unity.

Similarly, if we select the foot as the fundamental unit of length and again assume that $k = 1$, then Eq. (1.1) determines the unit of velocity as 1 ft/sec (one foot per second), since we have selected 1 foot as the unit of distance, and 1 second as the unit of time.

However, if we choose the unit of velocity as 1 mi/hr (one mile per hour), for example, then the factor k is no longer equal to unity. We, again, determine its value from the relationship:

$$\frac{\text{mi}}{\text{hr}} = k \frac{\text{ft}}{\text{sec}}$$

whence:

$$k = \frac{\text{mi/hr}}{\text{ft/sec}} = \frac{\text{mi . sec}}{\text{ft . hr}} = \frac{(5280 \text{ ft}). \text{ sec}}{\text{ft.}(3600 \text{ sec})} = \frac{22}{15}$$

Thus, if we express the length in feet, the time in seconds, and the velocity in miles per hour, the proportionality factor in Eq. (1.1) will be equal to 22/15, and the velocity equation will be:

$$v = \frac{22}{15} \cdot \frac{s}{t} \tag{1.3a}$$

Again, we see that it is not advisable to select the unit of measurement for velocity on an arbitrary basis.

The same procedure applies to the choice of units for other physical quantities such as acceleration, force, energy, etc., and equations reflecting physical laws should be used for proper selection of units of measurement.

The formulas and equations which are used to determine the units of measurement of any physical quantity are termed *fundamental equations*.

The equation $v = \frac{s}{t}$ is the fundamental equation for the unit of velocity. Similarly, the equation $F = m \cdot a$ is fundamental for the unit of force, $W = F \cdot s$ is the fundamental equation for the unit of work, $P = \frac{W}{t}$ is fundamental for the unit of power, etc.

Physical quantities whose units of measurement have been selected independently (in our case, length, mass, and time) are termed the *fundamental quantities of the system*. The units of measurement of fundamental quantities are likewise termed the *fundamental units of the system.**

Physical quantities whose units are obtained from fundamental equations are said to be *derived quantities*, and the units for measuring them are referred to as *derived units*. These quantities have been termed derived because they are derived from fundamental quantities (just as their units of measurement are expressed in terms of fundamental units).

The aggregate set of the units of fundamental quantities and the units of all derived quantities is termed a *system of units of measurement of physical quantities*, or simply a *system of units*. Many years of experience have shown that the most convenient systems are those based on three or four fundamental units.

The first method of formulating systems of units was presented by Gauss. His system was intended for the measurement of magnetic quantities and contained a unit of length, the millimeter, a unit of mass, the milligram, and a unit of time, the second, as the fundamental units. Later, this system was enlarged with units for measuring electrical, thermal, light, and other quantities. Two of the fundamental units in the Gaussian system, the millimeter and the

---

*Not to be confused with the fundamental units of measurement for the given physical quantity.

milligram, were later replaced by the centimeter and the gram, and, because of the initial letters of the fundamental units, the system became known as the *cgs* system. The cgs system uses *length, mass,* and *time* as the fundamental quantities. The same quantities are also fundamental in another commonly used system—the *MKS* system, which has the following fundamental units: meter, kilogram, and second. Finally, length, mass, and time are also the fundamental quantities of the familiar British system (fundamental units: foot, pound, and second). The choice of fundamental units is determined solely by the application of the system to the given field of physics or engineering.

2. DIMENSIONS OF DERIVED QUANTITIES AND UNITS OF MEASUREMENT

If we choose the length l, the mass m, and the time t as our fundamental quantities (as in the cgs and British systems), then we can express all other mechanical quantities by means of the fundamental equations. To accomplish this, we must first arrange the equations expressing mechanical laws in a series satisfying the following two conditions:

a) the first equation in the series must define a quantity in terms of fundamental quantities only;

b) each subsequent equation must define a quantity expressed in terms of the fundamental quantities and of those derived quantities that have already been determined by the preceding equations in the series.

For example, the following series of equations satisfies such conditions:

$$v = \frac{s}{t}, \ a = \frac{v}{t}, \ F = ma, \ p = \frac{F}{S}, \ W = F \cdot s, \ P = \frac{W}{t}, \ I = mr^2, \ \text{etc.}$$

Each of these equations either shows directly the relationship between the derived and the fundamental quantity, or else indicates a means of determining this dependence.

Thus, the equation $I = mr^2$ shows that the moment of inertia of a point mass about the axis of rotation is a linear function of the mass, and is proportional to the square of the distance between the point and the axis.* Similarly, a direct relationship between the derived and the fundamental quantities can be established by:

$$v = \frac{s}{t}$$

The remaining equations in the given series do not show the direct dependence of the derived on the fundamental quantities. However,

---

*The moment of inertia is more thoroughly defined in Chapter II.

such dependence can be easily found by expressing the derived quantities appearing on the right-hand side of these equations in terms of fundamental ones.

For example, in the acceleration equation, we may express the velocity in terms of length and time:

$$a = \frac{v}{t} = \frac{s}{t \cdot t} = \frac{s}{t^2} = s \cdot t^{-2}$$

This equation clearly indicates that acceleration is directly proportional to the distance traveled and inversely proportional to the square of the time. All other derived quantities can be expressed in terms of fundamental quantities by exactly the same method.

A formula expressing the dependence of a derived quantity on fundamental quantities is termed *a dimensional equation of a derived quantity*, or, simply, the *dimension of the derived quantity*.

Let us choose the following symbols to denote the dimensions of fundamental quantities: L for length, M for mass, and T for time. It is customary to distinguish the quantities from their dimensions by enclosing the former in brackets. For example, the dimensions of acceleration are given by:

$$[a] = \frac{[v]}{[t]} = \frac{LT^{-1}}{T} = LT^{-2}$$

The dimensions of force are defined by:

$$[F] = [m] \cdot [a] = MLT^{-2} = LMT^{-2}$$

etc.

The concept of dimensions of quantities explained above gives rise to a similar concept of the *dimensions of units*.

If we express the fundamental quantities appearing in a dimensional equation of a derived quantity in terms of their units of measurement, we get a dimensional equation for the derived unit (the dimensions of the derived unit).

Thus, for example, if we replace L, M, and T by their units of measurement in the MKS system, that is, the meter, kilogram, and second, then, from the following equation:

$$[F] = LMT^{-2}$$

we find the dimensions of the unit of force in this system to be $m \times kg \times sec^{-2}$ [this unit is also known as the *newton* (N)].

We might have adopted the following mathematical notation for the phrase "the dimensions of the unit of force (the newton) are equal to $m \times kg \times sec^{-2}$":

$$[N] = kg \times m \times sec^{-2}$$

However, such notation would be most inconvenient to describe units which are not known by any special term. For example, the dimensions of the unit of velocity in the MKS system would have to be expressed as:

$$[\text{unit of velocity}] = m \times \sec^{-1}$$

Hence, we agree to designate the dimensions of a unit of measurement of any quantity in the same manner as we designate the dimensions of the quantity itself, that is, by a symbol enclosed in square brackets. For example, $[v] = m \times \sec^{-1}$ denotes the dimensions of the unit of velocity in the MKS system, $[F] = kg \times m \times \sec^{-2}$ denotes the dimensions of the unit of force in the MKS system, etc.

The dimensional equation shows the dependence of the magnitude of an arbitrary unit on the fundamental units. By means of the dimensional equations, we can determine the ratio of the derived units in various systems.

The dimensional equation for work:

$$[W] = L^2 M T^{-2}$$

shows that the unit of work is directly proportional to the unit of mass and to the square of the unit of length, while it is inversely proportional to the square of the unit of time. It now becomes evident that the unit of work in the *MKS* system is greater than the unit of work in the cgs system by a factor of $(1000)^1 \times (100)^2 \times 1^{-2} = 10^7$.

In the same way, if we note that 1 kg = 2.20 lb (all conversions from the British to the MKS or cgs systems will be taken with accuracy to within three significant figures) and 1 m = 3.28 ft, we find that the unit of work in the MKS system is greater than the unit of work in the British system (the foot-poundal) by a factor of $(2.2)^1 \times (3.28)^2 \times 1^{-2} = 23.7$.

The dimensional equation for volume, $[V] = L^3$, shows that the unit of volume is directly proportional to the third power of the unit of length. If we replace the unit of length expressed in meters by the same unit in centimeters, the unit of volume will be reduced by a factor of one million, that is, 1 cm is equal to $\left(\frac{1}{100} \ m\right)^3 = \frac{1}{1,000,000} \ m^3$.

The dimensions of a physical quantity or the dimensions of its unit usually completely characterize the quantity itself. It is only in a very few cases that two or more quantities have the same dimensions. Two such exceptions are cited here.

In the cgs system both length and capacitance have the same dimensions:

$$[l] = L, \ [C] = L$$

Also, in this system, the moment of a force and work have the same dimensions:

$$[M] = L^2 M T^{-2}$$
$$[W] = L^2 M T^{-2}$$

3. PROPORTIONALITY FACTOR IN PHYSICAL FORMULAS

It was shown above that the proportionality factor in physical equations depends on the choice of the units. We will consider this dependence in greater detail in the following sections.

1. PROPORTIONALITY FACTOR IN FUNDAMENTAL EQUATIONS

The proportionality factor in fundamental equations is always a dimensionless quantity. The numerical value of this factor is:

a) equal to unity if all the quantities are expressed in units of one and the same system;

b) different from unity if the quantities in the equation are expressed in different systems of units.

It was shown in Section 1 that if we express the length in meters, the time in seconds, and the velocity in kilometers per hour, the proportionality factor in the velocity equation (1.1) is equal to 5/18.

It is easily demonstrated that when the length is given in kilometers, the time in seconds, and the velocity in meters per second, $k = 50/3$; and if the length is expressed in centimeters, the time in hours, and the velocity in meters per second, then $k = (5/18) \cdot 10^{-5}$, etc.

Let us consider the significance of the numerical value of the proportionality factor in the fundamental equation, and return to the example given in Section 1.

In Eq. (1.3):

$$v = \frac{5}{18} \cdot \frac{s}{t}$$

the left-hand side gives the velocity expressed in km/hr, and the right-hand side gives the distance in meters, divided by the time in seconds; that is:

$$\text{km/hr} = \frac{5}{18} \text{ m/sec}$$

Hence, the following ratio can be set up:

$$\frac{\text{km/hr}}{\text{m/sec}} = \frac{5}{18} \text{ or } \frac{\text{m/sec}}{\text{km/hr}} = \frac{18}{5}$$

This ratio shows that the unit of velocity in km/hr is 5/18 of the unit of velocity in m/sec, or that the unit of velocity in m/sec is greater than the unit of velocity in km/hr by a factor of 18/5. Analogously, we can find that km/min is greater than m/sec by a factor of 50/3, or that m/sec is greater than cm/hr by a factor of $(18/5) \cdot 10^5$, or that mi/hr is greater than ft/sec by a factor of 22/15.

Thus, the numerical value of the proportionality factor in fundamental equations indicates the ratio of two different units of measurement for the same quantity.

If we wish to eliminate the proportionality factor in the fundamental equations and avoid calculating it each time, we must express all physical quantities in the equation in units of one and the same system. Then, the result will also be obtained in units of that system. Adherence to this rule eliminates the rather frequent errors made by students in solving problems in physics and engineering, and enables us to write all the fundamental equations without including the proportionality factor $(k = 1)$.

2. PROPORTIONALITY FACTOR IN PHYSICAL FORMULAS WHICH ARE NOT FUNDAMENTAL EQUATIONS

Most physical formulas are considered to be fundamental equations. However, there are some physical formulas which are not fundamental equations (although they could be made fundamental equations by a change in the system of units).

For example, Newton's law of gravitation:

$$F = G \frac{m_1 \cdot m_2}{r^2} \tag{1.4}$$

could become a fundamental equation for the unit of force. If we assumed $G = 1$, $m_1 = m_2 = m = 1$ g, and $r = 1$ cm, we could adopt as the unit of force, in the cgs system, that force with which two point masses, each with a mass of 1 gram, attract each other at a distance of 1 cm. However, the unit of force has already been determined from Newton's second law, and, therefore, Newton's law of gravitation, even though it expresses force, cannot become the fundamental equation for the unit of force.

By the same token, Eq. (1.4) cannot be considered a fundamental equation for either the mass or length (which are contained in it) because the units of these quantities have been established by other equations.

Hence, the proportionality factor in Newton's law of gravitation could not be set equal to unity, and its numerical value had to be determined experimentally. By measuring the force of attraction between two spheres with masses m_1 and m_2 using a torsion balance, the numerical value of the proportionality factor can be determined from the following formula:

$$G = \frac{F \cdot r^2}{m_1 \cdot m_2}$$

This factor is also known as the *gravitation constant*.

The gravitation constant is not only different from unity, but it is also dimensional. Its dimensions in the cgs system are:

$$[G] = \frac{[F]\,[r^2]}{[m^2]} = \frac{cm \cdot g \cdot sec^{-2} \cdot cm^2}{g^2} = cm^3 \cdot g^{-1} \cdot sec^{-2}$$

The gravitation constant was first determined by Cavendish in 1798. According to present-day measurements, it is equal to:

$$G = (6.670 \pm 0.005) \cdot 10^{-8}\, cm^3/g \cdot sec^2$$

The value of the gravitation constant given here applies only to the cgs system. The numerical value of the constant is different in other systems.

We have thus demonstrated that the proportionality factor in physical formulas which are not fundamental equations differs from unity and is a dimensional quantity. The proportionality factors in these formulas are constants with a definite physical significance. For example, the gravitation constant gives the attraction between two point masses having a mass of 1 gram each and separated by a distance of 1 cm.

The number of dimensional coefficients in physical formulas depends on the number of fundamental units on which the system is based. As the number of fundamental units increases, the number of dimensional coefficients also increases, and the system becomes more cumbersome. Conversely, in a system with only a few fundamental units, the number of dimensional coefficients is also small. In such a system, however, another undesirable feature arises: as the number of fundamental units decreases, the number of derived units with the same dimensions increases and the system becomes more difficult to use.

As we pointed out above, the most suitable system of units for measuring mechanical quantities is based on three fundamental units: length, mass, and time; or length, force, and time. For measurement of quantities pertaining to molecular physics, a system with four fundamental units has proved most convenient, that is, length, mass, time, and temperature. To measure electromagnetic quantities, we also use systems consisting of four fundamental units.

4. SYSTEMS OF UNITS ADOPTED IN SCIENCE AND ENGINEERING

During the search for more rational systems of measurement, a variety of systems and independent units have been introduced in different countries at various times. This has given rise to major difficulties in international intercourse on problems in science and engineering.

International congresses (General Conferences on Weights and Measures) have been convened, at various times, for the purpose of systematizing units and introducing a single universal system of units. On the basis of agreements reached at these conferences, and also in accordance with its own requirements, interests, and traditions, each country determines the systems of units valid within its own territory.

In the English-speaking world, the following systems of units are most commonly used.

I. Systems of mechanical units.

a. The *MKS* system (practical),* the fundamental units of which are the meter, the kilogram-mass, and the second.

b. The *cgs* system (physical), the fundamental units of which are the centimeter, the gram-mass, and the second.

c. The British "absolute"** system (*f lbm s* system) the fundamental units of which are the foot, the pound-mass, and the second.

d. The British "gravitational" or *f lbf s* system (technical), the fundamental units of which are the foot, the pound-force, and the second. The unit of mass in the British "gravitational" system is the slug = 1 lb per ft per sec ^{2}. To convert from the unit of force in the British "absolute" system (the poundal) to the unit of force in the "gravitational" system (the pound or pound weight), we must multiply by 32.174 ft per sec^2, the acceleration of gravity.

e. The metric "gravitational" system *(MKGFS)*, the fundamental units of which are the meter, the kilogram-force, and the second.

II. Systems of electrical and magnetic units.

a. The absolute *MKSA* system, the fundamental units of which are the meter, the kilogram-mass, the second, and the ampere.

b. The absolute cgs (Gaussian) system, the fundamental units of which are the centimeter, the gram-mass, and the second, and in which the permittivity of empty space ε_0 and the permeability of empty space μ_0 are equal to unity.

c. The *cgs esu* system ($\varepsilon_0 = 1$).

d. The *cgs emu* system ($\mu_0 = 1$).

There are also several different systems in use for thermal units, light units, acoustic units, and units for X rays, gamma radiation, and radioactivity.

---

*The term "practical" is used because the MKS system is the one in everyday use in continental Europe and many other countries. In the English-speaking world, the MKS system is used primarily in science and engineering.

**The term "absolute" is usually used with respect to systems of units which are based on units of mass, length, and time. In the United States, fps is the most common textbook designation for this absolute system. In this text, in order to differentiate between the absolute system's pound mass and the gravitational system's pound force, the designations f lbm s and f lbf s are used.

Chapter II

SYSTEMS OF MECHANICAL UNITS

The systems of mechanical units, the cgs, MKS, metric gravitational (MKGFS), British absolute (f lbm s) and British gravitational (f lbf s) systems used at the present time are based on three fundamental quantities.

In formulating the cgs, MKS, f lbm s systems, the three fundamental quantities are length, mass, and time, and the systems are termed absolute.

In formulating the f lbf s and MKGFS systems, the fundamental quantities are length, force, and time.

In all systems of mechanical units the *radian* is taken as the unit plane angle, and the *steradian* as the unit solid angle.

The radian (rad) is the angle whose intercepted arc in a circle equals the radius of the circle.

The steradian is the solid angle (cone) whose vertex is at the center of a sphere and which cuts an area on the surface of the sphere numerically equal to the square of the sphere's radius.

1. THE MKS SYSTEM (PRACTICAL)

The MKS system was introduced in 1901 by an Italian engineer, Giovanni Giorgi. The name MKS was taken from the initial letters of the fundamental units. The word "practical" is added because almost all of the units in this system, both fundamental and derived, are widely employed in practice.

1. FUNDAMENTAL UNITS IN THE MKS SYSTEM

The fundamental units in the MKS system are:

The meter (m)—the unit of length. The meter is the distance between two lines on a platinum-iridium bar kept by the International Bureau of Weights and Measures, at atmospheric pressure and at 0°C.*

---

*To guard against loss or damage to the standard, it has been redefined in terms of the orange-red wavelength of light emitted by krypton under certain standard conditions.

The kilogram (kg)—the unit of mass. The kilogram is the mass of an international prototype kilogram (made of platinum) kept by the International Bureau of Weights and Measures;*

The second (sec)—the unit of time. The second is the interval of time equal to 1/86,400 of a mean solar day.**

2. DERIVED UNITS IN THE MKS SYSTEM

In order to form the MKS system, that is, in order to define the derived units in this system, let us arrange the formulas expressing mechanical laws into a series satisfying the conditions mentioned in Chapter I, Section 2. This series is shown in Table 1. By using the formulas in this series, we obtain units of measurement of mechanical quantities in the MKS system.

Velocity. The unit of velocity v is obtained from the equation:

$$v = k \frac{s}{t} \tag{2.1}$$

where s is the distance traveled by a body in uniform motion during the time t, and k is the proportionality factor (k will always denote the proportionality factor, unless otherwise indicated).

Assuming in (2.1) that $k = 1$, $s = 1$ m, and $t = 1$ sec, we find one unit of velocity $= 1 \times \frac{1 \text{ m}}{1 \text{ sec}} = 1 \frac{\text{m}}{\text{sec}}$.

It follows from the above that the dimensions of the unit of velocity in the MKS system are m $\cdot$ sec^{-1}.

In the MKS system, the unit of velocity is the uniform velocity at which a body travels a distance of 1 meter in 1 second.

Acceleration. The fundamental equation for acceleration is:

$$a = k \frac{\Delta v}{\Delta t} \tag{2.2}$$

where Δv is the change in the velocity during uniform acceleration taking place over the time Δt.

Setting $k = 1$, $\Delta v = 1 \frac{\text{m}}{\text{sec}}$, and $\Delta t = 1$ sec, we find:

$$\text{one unit of acceleration} = 1 \times \frac{1 \text{ m/sec}}{1 \text{ sec}} = 1 \frac{\text{m}}{\text{sec}^2}$$

In the MKS system, the unit of acceleration is the uniform acceleration at which the velocity changes $1 \frac{\text{m}}{\text{sec}}$ in 1 sec.

---

*The mass of one cubic decimeter of distilled water at 4°C was originally taken as the unit of mass—the kilogram.

**The International Astronomical Union gives the following definition: the (ephemeris) is equal to 1/31,556,925.975 of the tropical year for 1900.0 January 0d12h ephemeris time.

Table 1
Units of Measurement of Mechanical Quantities
in the MKS System

Quantity	Funda-mental equation	Unit of measurement	
		Name of unit	Dimensions
Velocity	$v = \dfrac{s}{t}$	—	$m \cdot sec^{-1}$
Acceleration	$a = \dfrac{s}{t}$	—	$m \cdot sec^{-2}$
Force	$F = m \cdot a$	newton	$m \cdot kg \cdot sec^{-2}$
Pressure (stress)	$p = \dfrac{F}{S}$	—	$m^{-1} \cdot kg \cdot sec^{-2}$
Density	$\rho = \dfrac{m}{V}$	—	$m^{-3} \cdot kg$
Specific weight	$d = \dfrac{w}{V}$	—	$m^{-2} \cdot kg \cdot sec^{-2}$
Specific volume	$V_0 = \dfrac{V}{m}$	—	$m^{3} \cdot kg^{-1}$
Impulse	$K = F \cdot t$	—	$m \cdot kg \cdot sec^{-1}$
Momentum	$K = m \cdot v$	—	$m \cdot kg \cdot sec^{-1}$
Work (energy)	$W = F \cdot s$	joule	$m^{2} \cdot kg \cdot sec^{-2}$
Power	$P = \dfrac{W}{t}$	watt	$m^{2} \cdot kg \cdot sec^{-3}$
Torque	$M = F \cdot r$	—	$m^{2} \cdot kg \cdot sec^{-2}$
Torque impulse	$L = M \cdot t$	—	$m^{2} \cdot kg \cdot sec^{-1}$
Moment of inertia	$I = m \cdot r^{2}$	—	$m^{2} \cdot kg$
Frequency	$f = \dfrac{1}{T}$	cycle per second	sec^{-1}
Angular velocity	$\omega = \dfrac{\varphi}{t}$	radian per second	sec^{-1}
Angular acceleration	$\epsilon = \dfrac{\omega}{t}$	—	sec^{-2}
Angular momentum	$L = I \cdot \omega$	—	$m^{2} \cdot kg \cdot sec^{-1}$

Equation (2.2) gives the dimensions of the unit of acceleration:

$$[a] = \frac{[v]}{[t]} = \frac{m \cdot sec}{sec} = m \cdot sec^{-2}$$

Force. We can find the unit of force F from Newton's second law:

$$F = km \cdot a \tag{2.3}$$

where m is the mass of the body and a is the acceleration imparted to the body by the force F.

Setting $k = 1$, $m = 1$ kg, and $a = 1$ m/sec^2 in Eq. (2.3), we find that:

$$\text{one unit of force} = 1 \cdot 1 \text{ kg} \cdot 1 \frac{\text{m}}{\text{sec}^2} = 1 \frac{\text{kg} \cdot \text{m}}{\text{sec}^2}$$

This unit of force is called the *newton*.

The newton (N) is the force which imparts an acceleration of 1 m/sec^2 to a mass of 1 kg.

It follows from Eq. (2.3) that the newton has the following dimensions:

$$[F] = [m] \, [a] = \text{kg} \cdot \text{m} \cdot \text{sec}^{-2} = \text{m} \cdot \text{kg} \cdot \text{sec}^{-2}*$$

Pressure (stress). The unit of pressure p is found from the equation:

$$p = k \frac{F}{S} \tag{2.4}$$

where F is the force uniformly distributed over the area S.

Assuming, in this formula, that $k = 1$, $F = 1$ N, and $S = 1$ m^2, we find that:

$$\text{one unit of pressure} = 1 \times \frac{1 \text{ N}}{1 \text{ m}^2} = 1 \frac{\text{N}}{\text{m}^2}$$

The unit of pressure is the uniformly distributed pressure exerted on a surface of 1 m^2 by a force equal to 1.

The dimensions of the unit of pressure are found from Eq. (2.4):

$$[p] = \frac{[F]}{[S]} = \frac{\text{m} \cdot \text{kg} \cdot \text{sec}^{-2}}{\text{m}^2} = \text{m}^{-1} \cdot \text{kg} \cdot \text{sec}^{-2}$$

Density. The fundamental equation for density ρ is:

$$\rho = k \frac{m}{V} \tag{2.5}$$

where m is the mass of a homogeneous body and V is the volume of the body.

Assuming, in Eq. (2.5), that $k = 1$, $m = 1$ kg, and $V = 1$ m^3, we find that:

$$\text{one unit of density} = 1 \times \frac{1 \text{ kg}}{1 \text{ m}^3} = 1 \frac{\text{kg}}{\text{m}^3}$$

---

*Let us agree that in giving the dimensions of units of measurement in any absolute system, we will write the fundamental units in the following order: units of length, units of mass, and units of time.

In the MKS system, the unit of density is the density of a homogeneous substance with a volume of 1 m³ and a mass of 1 kg.

The dimensions of the unit of density are:

$$[\rho] = \frac{[m]}{[V]} = \frac{kg}{m^3} = m^{-3} \cdot kg$$

Specific weight. The unit of specific weight d is found from the equation:

$$d = k\frac{w}{V} \tag{2.6}$$

where w is the weight of a homogeneous body and V is its volume.

Assuming, in this equation, that $k = 1$, $w = 1$ N, and $V = 1$ m³, we find that:

$$\text{one unit of specific weight} = 1 \times \frac{1 \text{ N}}{1 \text{ m}^3} = 1 \frac{N}{m^3}$$

In the MKS system, the unit of specific weight is the specific weight of a homogeneous substance, 1 m³ of which weighs 1 N.

The dimensions of specific weight are:

$$[d] = \frac{[w]}{[V]} = \frac{m \cdot kg \cdot sec^{-2}}{m^3} = m^{-2} \cdot kg \cdot sec^{-2}$$

Specific volume. The specific volume of a substance is the volume occupied by a unit mass of homogeneous matter. The specific volume V_0 is determined by the equation:

$$V_0 = k\frac{V}{m} \tag{2.7}$$

where V is the volume occupied by a mass m of homogeneous matter.

Assuming, in Eq. (2.7), that $k = 1$, $V = 1$ m³, and $m = 1$ kg, we find that:

$$\text{one unit of specific volume} = 1 \times \frac{1 \text{ m}^3}{1 \text{ kg}} = 1\frac{m^3}{kg}$$

In the MKS system, the unit of specific volume is the specific volume of a homogeneous substance, 1 kg of which occupies a volume of 1 m³.

The dimensions of the unit of specific volume are:

$$[V_0] = \frac{[V]}{[m]} = \frac{m^3}{kg} = m^3 \cdot kg^{-1}$$

From the density equation (2.5) and specific volume equation (2.7), as well as from their dimensions, it is easy to see that the specific volume is the reciprocal of the density.

Impulse. The unit of impulse K is determined from the equation:

$$K = kF \cdot \Delta t \tag{2.8}$$

where F is the force acting on a body for a time Δt.

Substituting $k = 1$, $F = 1$ N, and $\Delta t = 1$ sec into Eq. (2.8), we find that:

one unit of impulse $= 1 \cdot 1$ N $\cdot 1$ sec $= 1$ N $\cdot$ sec

In the MKS system, the unit of impulse is the impulse caused by the action of a constant force of 1 N for 1 sec.

The dimensions of the unit of measurement of impulse are:

$$[K] = [F][\Delta t] = \text{m} \cdot \text{kg} \cdot \text{sec}^{-2} \cdot \text{sec} = \text{m} \cdot \text{kg} \cdot \text{sec}^{-1}$$

Momentum. The unit of momentum K is found from the equation:

$$K = k \cdot m \cdot \Delta v \tag{2.9}$$

where m is the mass of the body and Δv is the change in velocity of the body.

Assuming, in Eq. (2.9), that $k = 1$, $m = 1$ kg, and $\Delta v = 1$ m/sec, we get:

one unit of momentum $= 1 \cdot 1$ kg $\cdot 1 \dfrac{\text{m}}{\text{sec}} = 1 \dfrac{\text{kg} \cdot \text{m}}{\text{sec}}$

In the MKS system, the unit of momentum is taken as the momentum possessed by a body with a mass of 1 kg moving at a velocity of 1 m/sec.

The dimensions of momentum are:

$$[K] = [m][v] = \text{kg} \cdot \text{m} \cdot \text{sec}^{-1} = \text{m} \cdot \text{kg} \cdot \text{sec}^{-1}$$

Comparison of the dimensions of impulse and momentum shows that they are the same.

This also follows from the well-known formula in mechanics:

$$F \cdot \Delta t = m \cdot \Delta v$$

Work (energy). The fundamental equation from which we can determine the unit of work W is:

$$W = kF \cdot s \cdot \cos \alpha \tag{2.10}$$

where F is a constant force acting on a body, s is the distance traveled by the body due to the effect of this force, and α is the angle between the direction of the force and the direction of motion.

Assuming, in Eq. (2.10), that $k = 1$, $F = 1$ N, $s = 1$ m, $\alpha = 0°$, we get:

$$\text{one unit of work} = 1 \cdot 1 \text{ N} \cdot 1 \text{ m} = 1 \text{ N} \cdot \text{m}$$

This unit of work is called a *joule*.

The joule (J) is the work done by a constant force of 1 N acting on a body over a distance of 1 m in the direction of the force.

The dimensions of the unit of work, in the MKS system, are:

$$[W] = [F][s] = \text{m} \cdot \text{kg} \cdot \text{sec}^{-2} \cdot \text{m} = \text{m}^2 \cdot \text{kg} \cdot \text{sec}^{-2}$$

Joules are also used to measure other forms of energy. Hence, the unit of work (energy) can also be determined from:

a) the kinetic energy equation for forward motion of a body:

$$\text{K.E.} = k \frac{m \cdot v^2}{2} \tag{2.11}$$

where m is the mass of the body moving at a velocity v;

b) the potential energy equation for a raised body:

$$\text{P.E.} = kmg \cdot H \tag{2.12}$$

where m is the mass of the body, g is the acceleration of gravity, and H is the height of the body above the surface of the earth;

c) the potential energy equation for a deformed body:

$$\text{P.E.} = k \frac{k' (\Delta L)^2}{2} \tag{2.13}$$

where ΔL is the absolute elongation of the body and k' is the coefficient of rigidity, which expresses the force per unit length required to deform the body, and is measured, in the MKS system, in N/m.

The reader may wish to derive the unit of energy in the MKS system from Eqs. (2.11), (2.12), and (2.13), and to prove that these equations can also be the fundamental ones for the unit of work.

Power. The unit of power P is determined from the equation:

$$P = k \frac{W}{t} \tag{2.14}$$

where W is the work done in the time t.

Assuming, in this formula, that $k = 1$, $W = 1$ J, and $t = 1$ sec, we find that:

$$\text{one unit of power} = 1 \times \frac{1 \text{ joule}}{1 \text{ sec}} = 1 \frac{\text{joule}}{\text{sec}}$$

This unit is called a watt.

The watt (w) is the power at which 1 J of work is done in 1 sec. The dimensions of the unit of power are:

$$[P] = \frac{[W]}{[t]} = \frac{m^2 \cdot kg \cdot sec^{-2}}{sec} = m^2 \cdot kg \cdot sec^{-3}$$

Torque (moment of force). The fundamental equation for the torque M is:

$$M = kF \cdot r \qquad (2.15)$$

where F is the force and r is the arm of the force F, that is, the shortest distance between the axis of rotation and the direction of the force.

Assuming, in Eq. (2.15), that $k = 1$, $F = 1$ N, and $r = 1$ m, we find that:

one unit of torque = 1 N $\cdot$ 1 m = 1 N $\cdot$ m

In the MKS system, the unit torque is taken as the torque exerted by 1 newton with an arm equal to 1 m.

The dimensions of the unit of torque are:

$$[M] = [F][r] = m \cdot kg \cdot sec^{-2} \cdot m = m^2 \cdot kg \cdot sec^{-2}$$

From the equations for work (2.10) and force (2.15), we can see that these quantities have the same dimensions.

Torque impulse. The unit of measurement for the torque impulse is found from the fundamental equation:

$$L = kM \cdot t \qquad (2.16)$$

where M is the torque and t is the time over which the torque acts.

Assuming, in Eq. (2.16), that $k = 1$, $M = 1$ N $\cdot$ m, and $t = 1$ sec, we find that:

1 MKS $(L)^* = 1$ N $\cdot$ m $\cdot$ 1 sec = 1 N $\cdot$ m $\cdot$ sec

The unit of torque impulse, in the MKS system, is taken as the torque impulse exerted by a torque of 1 N $\cdot$ m acting for 1 sec.

The dimensions of the unit of torque impulse are:

$$[L] = [M][t] = m^2 \cdot kg \cdot sec^{-2} \cdot sec = m^2 \cdot kg \cdot sec^{-1}$$

Moment of inertia. The unit of moment of inertia is found from the equation:

---

*Let us agree to designate the units of measurement which do not have a name by the abbreviation for the system of units with the addition of a symbol, in parentheses, for the value being measured. Thus, "1 MKS *(L)*" replaces the words "one unit of torque impulse in the MKS system."

Similar designations are employed extensively in the cgs esu and cgs emu electromagnetic systems. For purposes of abbreviation, it is advisable to do likewise in other systems of units.

$$I = km \cdot r^2 \tag{2.17}$$

where m is the mass of a particle and r is the distance between the particle and the rotation axis.

Assuming, in Eq. (2.17), that $k = 1$, $m = 1 \, \text{kg}$, and $r = 1$ m, we find that:

one unit of moment of inertia = $1 \cdot 1 \, \text{kg} \cdot 1 \, \text{m}^2 = 1 \, \text{kg} \cdot \text{m}^2$

In the MKS system, the unit of moment of inertia is taken as the moment of inertia possessed by a particle with a mass of 1 kg situated at a distance of 1 m from the rotation axis.

The dimensions of the unit of moment of inertia are:

$$[I] = [m] \, [r^2] = \text{kg} \cdot \text{m}^2 = \text{m}^2 \cdot \text{kg}$$

Frequency. The frequency of a periodic process is inversely proportional to the period and is determined by the formula:

$$\nu = \frac{1}{T} \tag{2.18}$$

where T is the period, that is, the time in which one cycle of the periodic process is completed.

It follows from this formula that the unit of measurement of frequency is 1/sec, while its dimension is sec^{-1}.

Angular velocity [cyclic (angular) frequency]. The angular velocity ω is determined from the equation:

$$\omega = k \frac{\varphi}{t} \tag{2.19}$$

where φ is the central angle described by the radius vector of a point in uniform circular motion in the time t.

Setting $k = 1$, $\varphi = 1$ rad, and $t = 1$ sec, we find that:

one unit of angular velocity = $1 \times \dfrac{1 \, \text{rad}}{1 \, \text{sec}} = 1 \dfrac{\text{rad}}{\text{sec}}$

The unit of angular velocity is taken as the angular velocity at which the radius vector of a point in uniform circular motion describes a central angle of 1 radian in 1 sec.

It follows from Eq. (2.19) that the dimension of angular velocity is sec^{-1}.

The angular velocity may also be measured in rps (revolutions per second) and rpm (revolutions per minute).

Angular acceleration. The unit of measurement of angular acceleration is found from the equation:

$$\varepsilon = k \frac{\Delta \omega}{\Delta t} \tag{2.20}$$

where $\Delta \omega$ is the change in angular velocity of a point in circular motion in time Δt.

Assuming, in Eq. (2.20), that $k = 1$, $\Delta\omega = 1$ rad/sec, and $\Delta t = 1$ sec, we find that:

$$\text{one unit of angular acceleration} = 1 \times \frac{1 \text{ rad/sec}}{1 \text{ sec}} = 1 \frac{\text{rad}}{\text{sec}^2}$$

As the unit of angular acceleration, we take the angular acceleration at which a point in circular motion changes its angular velocity by 1 rad/sec in one second.

The dimension of angular acceleration, as follows from Eq. (2.20), is sec^{-2}.

The angular acceleration is also measured in rps^2 and rpm^2.

Angular momentum. The unit of measurement of angular momentum L is determined from the equation:

$$L = k \cdot I \cdot \omega \tag{2.21}$$

where I is the moment of inertia of the body and ω is its angular velocity.

Assuming that $k = 1$, $I = 1 \text{ kg} \cdot \text{m}^2$, and $\omega = 1$ rad/sec, we find that:

$$1 \text{ MKS } (L) = 1 \cdot 1 \text{ kg} \cdot \text{m}^2 \cdot 1 \frac{\text{rad}}{\text{sec}} = 1 \frac{\text{kg} \cdot \text{m}^2 \cdot \text{rad}}{\text{sec}}$$

The unit of angular momentum in the MKS system is taken as the angular momentum of a body with a moment of inertia of 1 kg $\cdot$ m^2 with respect to the axis around which it rotates uniformly at an angular velocity of 1 rad/sec.

The dimensions of angular momentum are:

$$[L] = [I][\omega] = \text{m}^2 \cdot \text{kg} \cdot \text{sec}^{-1}$$

2. THE CGS SYSTEM (PHYSICAL)

The cgs system was developed by British scientists on the basis of a proposal advanced by Thomson. It was adopted as an international system at the First International Congress of Electricians in 1881. The term *cgs* stems from the initial letters of the fundamental units. The word *physical* is added because the units in this system are used mainly in physics.

1. FUNDAMENTAL UNITS IN THE CGS SYSTEM

The fundamental units in the cgs system are:

The centimeter (cm)—the unit of length. The centimeter is one hundredth of a meter.

The gram (g)—the unit of mass. The gram is one thousandth of a kilogram.

The second (sec)—the unit of time.*

---

* See definition given in the previous section on the MKS system.

Table 2

Units of Measurement of Mechanical Quantities in the cgs System

Quantity	Funda-mental equation	Unit of measurement		
		Name of unit	Abbre-via-tion	Dimensions
Velocity	$v = \dfrac{s}{t}$	—	$\dfrac{cm}{sec}$	$cm \cdot sec^{-1}$
Acceleration	$a = \dfrac{v}{t}$	—	$\dfrac{cm}{sec^2}$	$cm \cdot sec^{-2}$
Force	$F = m \cdot a$	dyne	dyne	$cm \cdot g \cdot sec^{-2}$
Pressure	$w = \dfrac{F}{S}$	barye	$\dfrac{dyne}{cm^2}$	$cm^{-1} \cdot g \cdot sec^{-2}$
Density	$\rho = \dfrac{m}{V}$	—	$\dfrac{g}{cm^3}$	$cm^{-3} \cdot g$
Specific weight	$d = \dfrac{w}{V}$	—	$\dfrac{dyne}{cm^3}$	
Specific volume	$V_0 = \dfrac{V}{m}$	—	—	$cm^3 \cdot g^{-1}$
Impulse	$K = F \cdot t$	—	—	$cm \cdot g \cdot sec^{-1}$
Momentum	$K = m \cdot v$	—	—	$cm \cdot g \cdot sec^{-2}$
Work (energy)	$W = F \cdot s$	erg	—	$cm^2 \cdot g \cdot sec^{-2}$
Power	$P = \dfrac{A}{t}$	—	$\dfrac{erg}{sec}$	$cm^2 \cdot g \cdot sec^{-3}$
Torque	$M = F \cdot r$	—	—	$cm^2 \cdot g \cdot sec^{-2}$
Torque impulse	$L = M \cdot t$	—	—	$cm^2 \cdot g \cdot sec^{-1}$
Moment of inertia	$I = m \cdot r^2$	—	—	$cm^2 \cdot g$
Frequency	$f = \dfrac{1}{T}$	cycle per second	cps	sec^{-1}
Angular velocity	$\omega = \dfrac{\varphi}{t}$	—	$\dfrac{rad}{sec}$	sec^{-1}
Angular acceleration	$\epsilon = \dfrac{\omega}{t}$	—	$\dfrac{rad}{sec^2}$	sec^{-2}
Angular momentum	$L = I \cdot \omega$	—	—	$cm^2 \cdot g \cdot sec^{-1}$

2. DERIVED UNITS IN THE CGS SYSTEM

The derived units and their dimensions in the cgs system can be obtained in the same manner as indicated for the MKS system.

The sequence of the fundamental equations is shown in Table 2.

The structure of the cgs system is similar to that of the MKS system, since in both systems the fundamental quantities are length, mass, and time.

The reader can derive the units of measurement and their dimensions in the cgs system by using the fundamental equations in Table 2.

Some of the units of measurement in the cgs system have special names. They are defined as follows:

The *dyne* is the force which is imparted to a mass of one gram by an acceleration of 1 cm/sec^2.

The *barye* is the pressure at which a force of 1 dyne is uniformly distributed over an area of 1 cm^2.

The *erg* is the work which is done by a force of 1 dyne over a distance of 1 centimeter.

3. THE METRIC GRAVITATIONAL (MKGFS) SYSTEM (TECHNICAL)

The metric gravitational (MKGFS) system was introduced in the second half of the 19th century. The fundamental quantities in this system are length, force, and time. Mass in the MKGFS system is a derived quantity, not a fundamental one as in the MKS and cgs systems considered above.

Like the other systems, this one derives its name from the initial letters of its fundamental units.

The metric gravitational system is of limited application. Its units are not used in electricity, magnetism, or certain other branches of physics. It is most commonly used in engineering. Hence, the term "technical" is added to its name.

1. FUNDAMENTAL UNITS IN THE MKGFS SYSTEM

The fundamental units in the metric gravitation system are:

The meter (m)—the unit of length (defined earlier).

The kilogram-force (KGF)—the unit of force.

The kilogram-force is the force due to gravity exerted by a body with a mass of 1 kg (in other words, the weight of a mass of 1 kg) at the latitude of Paris at sea level.

The second (sec)—the unit of time (defined earlier).

2. DERIVED UNITS IN THE MKGFS SYSTEM

In the formulation of the MKGFS system, the arrangement of the fundamental equations differs slightly from the arrangement adopted for the MKS and cgs systems. In the MKGFS system, Newton's second law is a fundamental equation for mass, rather than for force.

The dimensions of most of the physical quantities and the units for their measurement are also expressed in an essentially different manner (the units differ in principle).

The technical system is often confused with the practical system, since the units of length (m), velocity (m/sec), acceleration (m/sec²), and certain other quantities are the same for both. Furthermore, historically, the unit of mass in the practical system and the unit of force in the technical system have the same name—the kilogram. This fact is the cause of frequent misunderstanding in solving physical problems. It should, therefore, be kept firmly in mind that the kilogram (kg) is the unit of mass in the MKS system (practical), whereas the kilogram-force (kgf) is the unit of force in the MKGFS system (technical).

The order of the fundamental equations adopted in the MKGFS system is shown in Table 3.

Using these fundamental equations, we can find the derived units of the MKGFS system. We will only derive those units which differ in dimensions from the corresponding units in the MKS system.

Mass. The unit of mass m can be obtained from Newton's second law:

$$F = kma$$

from which:

$$m = \frac{1}{k}\frac{F}{a} \qquad (2.22)$$

Setting $k = 1$, $F = 1$ kgf, and $a = 1$ m/sec², we find that:

$$\text{one unit of mass} = 1 \times \frac{1 \text{ kgf}}{1 \text{ m/sec}^2} = 1 \frac{\text{kgf} \cdot \text{sec}^2}{\text{m}}$$

This unit is termed the *metric slug*.

The metric slug is the mass to which a force of 1 kgf imparts an acceleration of 1 m/sec².

The dimensions of this unit, as follows from Eq. (2.22), are $m^{-1} \cdot \text{kgf} \cdot \text{sec}^2$.

Pressure. The unit of pressure is determined from the equation:

$$p = k\frac{F}{S} \qquad (2.23)$$

where F is a force uniformly distributed over the area S.

Setting $k = 1$, $F = 1$ kgf, and $S = 1$ m², we find that:

$$\text{one unit of pressure} = 1 \times \frac{1 \text{ kgf}}{1 \text{ m}^2} = 1 \frac{\text{kgf}}{\text{m}^2}$$

The unit of pressure in the MKGFS system is taken as the uniform pressure exerted by a force of 1 kgf over an area of 1 m².

Table 3

Units of Measurement of Mechanical Quantities in the MKGFS System

Quantity	Funda-mental equation	Unit of measurement		
		Name of unit	Abbrevi-ation	Dimensions
Velocity	$v = \dfrac{s}{t}$	—	$\dfrac{m}{sec}$	$m \cdot sec^{-1}$
Acceleration	$a = \dfrac{v}{t}$	—	$\dfrac{m}{sec^2}$	$m \cdot sec^{-2}$
Mass	$m = \dfrac{F}{a}$	metric slug	$\dfrac{kgf \cdot sec^2}{m}$	$m^{-1} \cdot kgf \cdot sec^2$
Pressure	$P = \dfrac{F}{S}$	—	$\dfrac{kgf}{m^2}$	$m^{-2} \cdot kgf$
Specific weight	$d = \dfrac{w}{V}$	—	$\dfrac{kgf}{m^3}$	$m^{-3} \cdot kgf$
Density	$\rho = \dfrac{m}{V}$	—	$\dfrac{kgf \cdot sec^2}{m^4}$	$m^{-4} \cdot kgf \cdot sec^2$
Specific volume	$V_0 = \dfrac{V}{m}$	—	—	$m^4 \cdot kgf^{-1} \cdot sec^{-2}$
Impulse	$K = F \cdot t$	—	—	$kgf \cdot sec$
Momentum	$K = m \cdot v$	—	—	$kgf \cdot sec$
Work (energy)	$W = F \cdot s$	kilogram-meter	$kgf \cdot m$	$m \cdot kgf$
Power	$P = \dfrac{W}{t}$	—	$\dfrac{kgf \cdot m}{sec}$	$m \cdot kgf \cdot sec^{-1}$
Torque	$M = F \cdot r$	—	—	$m \cdot kgf$
Torque impulse	$L = M \cdot t$	—	—	$m \cdot kgf \cdot sec$
Moment of inertia	$I = mr^2$	—	—	$m \cdot kgf \cdot sec^2$
Frequency	$f = \dfrac{1}{T}$	cycle per second	$\dfrac{cps}{sec}$	sec^{-1}
Angular velocity	$\omega = \dfrac{\varphi}{t}$	—	$\dfrac{rad}{sec}$	sec^{-1}
Angular acceleration	$\epsilon = \dfrac{\omega}{t}$	—	$\dfrac{rad}{sec^2}$	sec^{-2}
Angular momentum	$L = I\omega$	—	—	$m \cdot kgf \cdot sec$

As follows from Eq. (2.23), the dimensions of this unit are $m^{-2} \cdot kgf$.

Specific weight. The fundamental equation for the unit of specific weight d is:

$$d = k\frac{w}{V} \tag{2.24}$$

where w is the weight of a homogeneous body occupying a volume V.

Assuming, in Eq. (2.24), that $k = 1$, $w = 1$ kgf, and $V = 1$ m³, we find that:

$$\text{one unit of specific weight} = 1 \times \frac{1 \text{ kgf}}{1 \text{ m}^3} = 1\frac{\text{kgf}}{\text{m}^3}$$

In the MKGFS system, the unit of specific weight is the specific weight of a homogeneous body, 1 m³ of which weighs 1 kgf.

Equation (2.24) gives us the dimensions of the unit of specific weight—m⁻³ · kgf.

Density. The unit of density in the MKGFS system is determined by the equation:

$$\rho = k\frac{m}{V} \tag{2.25}$$

where m is the mass of a homogeneous body and V is the volume of this body.

Assuming, in this formula, that $k = 1$, $m = 1$ metric slug, and $V = 1$ m³, we find that:

$$\text{one unit of density} = 1 \times \frac{1 \text{ metric slug}}{1 \text{ m}^3} = 1\frac{\text{metric slug}}{\text{m}^3}$$

In the MKGFS system the unit of density is the density of a homogeneous substance, 1 metric slug of which occupies 1 m³.

The dimensions of the unit of density are:

$$[\rho] = \frac{[m]}{[V]} = \frac{\text{m}^{-1} \cdot \text{kgf} \cdot \text{sec}^2}{\text{m}^3} = \text{m}^{-4} \cdot \text{kgf} \cdot \text{sec}^2$$

Specific volume. The unit of specific volume V_0 is determined from the equation:

$$V_0 = k\frac{V}{m} \tag{2.26}$$

where V is the volume occupied by a homogeneous body of mass m.

Assuming, in this formula, that $k = 1$, $V = 1$ m³, and $m = 1$ metric slug, we find that:

$$\text{one unit of specific volume} = 1 \times \frac{1 \text{ m}^3}{1 \text{ metric slug}} = 1\frac{\text{m}^3}{\text{metric slug}}$$

In the MKGFS system the unit of specific volume is the specific volume of a homogeneous substance, 1 metric slug of which occupies a volume of 1 m³.

It follows from Eq. (2.26) that the dimensions of the unit of specific volume are:

$$[V_0] = \frac{[V]}{[m]} = \frac{m^3}{m^{-1} \cdot kgf \cdot sec^2} = m^4 \cdot kgf^{-1} \cdot sec^{-2}$$

Impulse. The fundamental equation for the unit of impulse K is the following:

$$K = kF \cdot \Delta t \qquad (2.27)$$

Assuming, in this equation, that $k = 1$, $F = 1$ kgf, and $\Delta t = 1$ sec, we find that:

one unit of impulse = $1 \cdot 1$ kgf $\cdot 1$ sec = 1 kgf $\cdot$ sec

In the MKGFS system, the unit of impulse is the impulse created by a force of 1 kgf acting for 1 sec.

As follows from Eq. (2.27), the dimensions of the unit of impulse in the MKGFS system are kgf $\cdot$ sec.

We find the same dimensions for the unit of momentum. This follows from the well-known equation in mechanics:

$$F\Delta t = \Delta(mv)$$

Work (energy). The unit of measure of work W can be determined from the equation:

$$W = kF \cdot s \cdot \cos\alpha \qquad (2.28)$$

where F is a constant force acting on a body over a distance s, and α is the angle between the direction of the force and the direction of motion of the body.

Assuming, in this formula, that $k = 1$, $F = 1$ kgf, $s = 1$ m, and $\alpha = 0°$, we find that:

one unit of work = $1 \cdot 1$ kgf $\cdot 1$ m $\cdot 1$ = 1 kgf $\cdot$ m

In the MKGFS system, the unit of work is called the kilogram-meter.

The kilogram-meter (kgfm) is the work done by a constant force of 1 kgf acting over a distance of 1 m (and in the same direction as the displacement).

The dimensions of the kilogram-meter are determined from Eq. (2.28):

$$[W] = [F][s] = kgf \cdot m = m \cdot kgf$$

Power. The unit of power P is determined from the equation:

$$P = k\frac{W}{t} \qquad (2.29)$$

where W is the work done in the time t.

Assuming, in this equation, that $k = 1$, $W = 1$ kgfm and $t = 1$ sec, we find that:

$$\text{one unit of power} = 1 \times \frac{1\ \text{kgfm}}{1\ \text{sec}} = 1\ \frac{\text{kgfm}}{\text{sec}}$$

In the MKGFS system the unit of power is the power at which 1 kgfm of work is done in 1 sec.

It follows from Eq. (2.29) that the dimensions of the unit of power in the MKGFS system are m $\cdot$ kgf $\cdot$ sec^{-1}.

Torque (moment of force). The fundamental equation of the unit of torque M is as follows:

$$M = kF \cdot r \qquad (2.30)$$

where F is the force and r is its arm.

Assuming, in (2.30), that $k = 1$, $F = 1$ kgf, and $r = 1$ m, we find that:

$$\text{one unit of torque} = 1 \cdot 1\ \text{kgf} \cdot 1\ \text{m} = 1\ \text{kgf} \cdot \text{m}$$

In the MKGFS system, the unit of torque is taken as the torque exerted by a force of 1 kgf with an arm of 1 m.

The dimensions of the unit of torque are the same as those of the unit of work—m $\cdot$ kgf.

Torque impulse. The unit of torque impulse L can be determined from the equation:

$$L = kM \cdot t \qquad (2.31)$$

where M is the torque and t is the time over which the torque acts.

Assuming, in this formula, that $k = 1$, $M = 1$ kgfm, and $t = 1$ sec, we find that:

$$\text{one unit of torque impulse} = 1 \cdot 1\ \text{kgfm} \cdot 1\ \text{sec} = 1\ \text{kgfm} \cdot \text{sec}$$

The unit of torque impulse in the MKGFS system is the torque impulse exerted by a torque of 1 kgfm acting for 1 sec.

The dimensions of the torque impulse are found from Eq. (2.31).

$$[L] = [M][t] = \text{m} \cdot \text{kgf} \cdot \text{sec}$$

Moment of inertia. The fundamental equation for the moment of inertia is as follows:

$$I = km \cdot r^2 \qquad (2.32)$$

where m is the mass of the particle and r is the distance between the particle and the rotation axis.

Assuming, in this equation, that $k = 1$, $m = 1$ metric slug, and $r = 1$ m, we find that:

1 unit of moment of inertia
$$= 1 \cdot 1 \text{ metric slug} \cdot 1 \text{ m}^2 = 1 \text{ metric slug} \cdot \text{m}^2$$

In the MKGFS system, the unit of moment of inertia is the moment of inertia which is possessed by a physical body with a mass of 1 metric slug rotating at a distance of 1 m from the rotation axis.

The dimensions of the unit of moment of inertia in the MKGFS system are found from Eq. (2.32):

$$[I] = [m][r^2] = \text{m}^{-1} \cdot \text{kgf} \cdot \text{sec}^2 \cdot \text{m}^2 = \text{m} \cdot \text{kgf} \cdot \text{sec}^2$$

Angular momentum. The unit of angular momentum L is determined from the equation:

$$L = kI\omega \qquad (2.33)$$

where I is the moment of inertia of a body rotating about an axis with an angular velocity ω.

Assuming, in (2.33), that $k = 1$, $I = 1$ m $\cdot$ kgf $\cdot$ sec^2, and $\omega = 1$ rad/sec, we find that:

$$1 \text{ MKGFS}(L) = 1 \cdot 1 \text{ m} \cdot \text{kgf} \cdot \text{sec}^2 \cdot 1 \frac{\text{rad}}{\text{sec}} = 1 \text{ m} \cdot \text{kgf} \cdot \text{sec} \cdot \text{rad}$$

The unit of angular momentum in the MKGFS system is taken as the angular momentum possessed by a body with a moment of inertia of 1 MKGFS (I) with respect to the axis about which it rotates at an angular velocity of 1 rad/sec.

The dimensions of the unit of angular momentum in the MKGFS system are m $\cdot$ kgf $\cdot$ sec $\cdot$ rad, or, if we omit the radians, as is often done, m $\cdot$ kgf $\cdot$ sec.

4. THE BRITISH ABSOLUTE (F LBM S) SYSTEM

In the English-speaking world, the measures of mass and length commonly employed for practical purposes are those of the British absolute (*f lbm s*) system. The designation *f lbm s* is taken from the fundamental units of the system. Because its fundamental units are length, mass, and time, the f lbm s system is completely analogous to the MKS system.

1. FUNDAMENTAL UNITS IN THE F LBM S SYSTEM

The fundamental units in the f lbm s system are:

The foot (ft)—the unit of length. The foot is defined as $\frac{1200}{3937}$ of a meter.

The pound-mass (lbm)—the unit of mass. The pound is equal to 453.59 grams.

The second (sec)—the unit of time, defined previously.

2. DERIVED UNITS IN THE F LBM S SYSTEM

In order to form the f lbm s system, that is, in order to define the derived units in this system, we use a series of formulas satisfying the conditions mentioned in Chapter I, Section 2. This series is shown in Table 4. By using the formulas in this series, we obtain the units of measurement of mechanical quantities in the f lbm s system.

Velocity. The unit of velocity v is obtained from the equation:

$$v = k\frac{s}{t} \qquad (2.34)$$

where k is proportionality constant (as usual) and s is the distance traveled by a body in uniform motion during a time t.

Assuming, in (2.34) that $k = 1$, $s = 1$ ft, and $t = 1$ sec, we find:

$$1 \text{ unit of velocity} = 1 \times \frac{1 \text{ ft}}{1 \text{ sec}} = 1 \frac{\text{ft}}{\text{sec}}$$

Thus, the dimensions of the unit of velocity in the f lbm s system are ft · sec^{-1}.

In the f lbm s system, the unit of velocity is the uniform velocity at which a body travels a distance of 1 ft in 1 sec.

Acceleration. The fundamental equation for acceleration is:

$$a = k\frac{\Delta v}{\Delta t} \qquad (2.35)$$

where Δv is the change in the velocity during uniform acceleration taking place over the time Δt.

Setting $k = 1$, $\Delta v = 1$ ft/sec, and $\Delta t = 1$ sec, we find:

Table 4

Units of Measurement of Mechanical Quantities in f lbm s System

Quantity	Fundamental equation	Unit of measurement		
		Name of unit	Abbreviation	Dimensions
Velocity	$v = \dfrac{s}{t}$	—	$\dfrac{\text{ft}}{\text{sec}}$	ft · sec^{-1}
Acceleration	$a = \dfrac{v}{t}$	—	$\dfrac{\text{ft}}{\text{sec}^2}$	ft · sec^{-2}
Force	$F = m \cdot a$	poundal	pdl	ft · lbm · sec^{-2}
Pressure (stress)	$p = \dfrac{F}{S}$	—	$\dfrac{\text{pdl}}{\text{ft}^2}$	ft^{-1} · lbm · sec^{-2}
Density	$\rho = \dfrac{m}{V}$	—	$\dfrac{\text{lbm}}{\text{ft}^3}$	ft^{-3} · lbm
Specific weight	$d = \dfrac{w}{V}$	—	$\dfrac{\text{pdl}}{\text{ft}^3}$	ft^{-2} · lbm · sec^{-2}
Specific volume	$V_0 = \dfrac{V}{m}$	—	$\dfrac{\text{ft}^3}{\text{lbm}}$	ft^3 · lbm^{-1}
Impulse	$K = F \cdot t$	—	pdl · sec	ft · lbm · sec^{-1}
Momentum	$K = m \cdot v$	—	pdl · sec	ft · lbm · sec^{-1}
Work (energy)	$W = F \cdot s$	—	ft · pdl	ft^2 · lbm · sec^{-2}
Power	$P = \dfrac{W}{t}$	—	$\dfrac{\text{ft} \cdot \text{pdl}}{\text{sec}}$	ft^2 · lbm · sec^{-3}
Torque	$M = F \cdot r$	—	—	ft^2 · lbm · sec^{-2}
Torque impulse	$L = M \cdot t$	—	—	ft^2 · lbm · sec^{-1}
Moment of inertia	$I = m \cdot r^2$	—	—	ft^2 · lbm
Frequency	$f = \dfrac{1}{T}$	cycles per sec	cps	sec^{-1}
Angular velocity	$\omega = \dfrac{\varphi}{t}$	radians per sec	$\dfrac{\text{rad}}{\text{sec}}$	sec^{-1}
Angular acceleration	$\epsilon = \dfrac{\omega}{t}$	—	—	sec^{-2}
Angular momentum	$L = I \cdot \omega$	—	—	ft^2 · lbm · sec^{-1}

$$1 \text{ unit of acceleration} = 1 \times \dfrac{1\,\dfrac{\text{ft}}{\text{sec}}}{1 \text{ sec}} = 1\,\dfrac{\text{ft}}{\text{sec}^2}$$

In the f lbm s system, the unit of acceleration is the uniform acceleration at which the velocity changes 1 ft/sec in 1 sec.

Equation (2.35) gives us the dimensions of the unit of acceleration:

$$[a] = \frac{[v]}{[t]} = \frac{ft \cdot sec^{-1}}{sec} = ft \cdot sec^{-2}$$

Force. We can find the unit of force F from the equation of Newton's second law:

$$F = km \cdot a \qquad (2.36)$$

where m is the mass of the body and a is the acceleration imparted to the body by the force F.

Setting $k = 1$, $m = 1$ lbm, and $a = 1$ ft/sec^2, we find that:

$$1 \text{ unit of force} = 1 \cdot 1 \text{ lbm} \cdot 1\frac{ft}{sec^2} = 1\frac{lbm \cdot ft}{sec^2}$$

This unit of force is called a *poundal*.

A poundal (pdl) is the force which imparts an acceleration of 1 ft/sec^2 to a mass of 1 lbm.

It follows from Eq. (2.36) that the poundal has the following dimensions:

$$[F] = [m][a] = lbm \cdot ft \cdot sec^{-2} = ft \cdot lbm \cdot sec^{-2}$$

Pressure (stress). The unit of pressure p is found from the equation:

$$p = k\frac{F}{S} \qquad (2.37)$$

where F is the force uniformly distributed over the area S.

Assuming, in this formula, that $k = 1$, $F = 1$ pdl, and $S = 1$ ft, we find that:

$$1 \text{ unit of pressure} = 1 \times \frac{1 \text{ pdl}}{1 \text{ ft}^2} = 1\frac{pdl}{ft^2}$$

The unit of pressure is the uniformly distributed pressure on 1 ft^2 exerted by a force equal to 1 pdl.

The dimensions of the unit of pressure are found from Eq. (2.37):

$$[p] = \frac{[F]}{[S]} = \frac{ft \cdot lbm \cdot sec^{-2}}{ft^2} = ft^{-1} \cdot lbm \cdot sec^{-2}$$

Density. The fundamental equation for density ρ is:

$$\rho = k\frac{m}{V} \qquad (2.38)$$

where m is the mass of a homogeneous body and V is the volume of the body.

Assuming, in Eq. (2.5), that $k = 1$, $m = 1$ lbm, and $V = 1$ ft^3, we find that:

$$1 \text{ unit of density} = 1 \times \frac{1 \text{ lbm}}{1 \text{ ft}^3} = 1 \frac{\text{lbm}}{\text{ft}^3}$$

In the f lbm s system, the unit of density is the density of a homogeneous substance of volume 1 ft^3 and mass 1 lbm.

The dimensions of this unit of density are:

$$[\rho] = \frac{[m]}{[V]} = \frac{\text{lbm}}{\text{ft}^3} = \text{ft}^{-3} \cdot \text{lbm}$$

Specific weight. The unit of specific weight d is found from the equation:

$$d = k \frac{w}{V} \tag{2.39}$$

where w is weight of a homogeneous body and V is its volume.

Assuming, in this equation, that $k = 1$, $w = 1$ pdl, and $V = 1$ ft^3, we find that:

$$1 \text{ unit of specific weight} = 1 \times \frac{1 \text{ pdl}}{1 \text{ ft}^3} = 1 \frac{\text{pdl}}{\text{ft}^3}$$

In the f lbm s system, the unit of specific weight is the specific weight of a homogeneous substance, 1 ft^3 of which weighs 1 pdl.

The dimensions of specific weight are:

$$[d] = \frac{[w]}{[V]} = \text{ft} \cdot \text{lbm} \cdot \text{sec}^{-2} \cdot \text{ft}^{-3} = \text{ft}^{-2} \cdot \text{lbm} \cdot \text{sec}^{-2}$$

Specific volume. The specific volume of a substance is the volume occupied by a unit mass of homogeneous matter. The specific volume V_0 is determined by the equation:

$$V_0 = k \frac{V}{m} \tag{2.40}$$

where V is the volume occupied by a mass m of homogeneous matter.

Assuming, in (2.7), that $k = 1$, $V = 1$ ft^3, and $m = 1$ lbm, we find that:

$$1 \text{ unit of specific volume} = 1 \times \frac{1 \text{ ft}^3}{1 \text{ lbm}} = 1 \frac{\text{ft}^3}{\text{lbm}}$$

In the f lbm s system, the unit of specific volume is the specific volume of a homogeneous substance, 1 lbm of which occupies a volume of 1 ft³.

The dimensions of the unit of specific volume are:

$$[V_0] = \frac{[V]}{[m]} = \frac{ft^3}{lbm} = ft^3 \cdot lbm^{-1}$$

Impulse. The unit of impulse K is determined from the equation:

$$K = kF \cdot \Delta t \tag{2.41}$$

where F is the force acting on a body for a time Δt.

Substituting $k = 1$, $F = 1$ pdl, and $\Delta t = 1$ sec into Eq. (2.41), we find that:

$$1 \text{ unit of impulse} = 1 \cdot 1 \text{ pdl} \cdot 1 \text{ sec} = 1 \text{ pdl} \cdot \text{sec}$$

In the f lbm s system, the unit of impulse is the impulse caused by the action of a constant force of 1 pdl for 1 sec.

The dimensions of the unit of measurement of impulse are:

$$[K] = [F][\Delta t] = ft \cdot lbm \cdot sec^{-2} \cdot sec = ft \cdot lbm \cdot sec^{-1}$$

Momentum. The unit of momentum K is found from the equation:

$$K = k \cdot m \cdot \Delta v \tag{2.42}$$

where m is the mass of the body and Δv is the change in velocity of the body.

Assuming, in Eq. (2.42), that $k = 1$, $m = 1$ lbm, and $\Delta v = 1$ ft/sec, we get:

$$1 \text{ unit of momentum} = 1 \cdot 1 \text{ lbm} \cdot 1 \frac{ft}{sec} = 1 \frac{lbm \cdot ft}{sec}$$

In the f lbm s system, the unit of momentum is taken as the momentum possessed by a body with a mass of 1 lbm moving at a velocity of 1 ft/sec.

The dimensions of momentum are:

$$[K] = [m][v] = lbm \cdot ft \cdot sec^{-1} = ft \cdot lbm \cdot sec^{-1}$$

We can easily see that the dimensions of impulse and momentum are the same.

This also follows from the well-known formula in mechanics:

$$F \cdot \Delta t = m \cdot \Delta v$$

Work (energy). The fundamental equation from which we can determine the unit of work W is:

$$W = kF \cdot s \cdot \cos \alpha \qquad (2.43)$$

where F is a constant force acting on a body, s is the distance traveled by the body due to the effect of this force, and α is the angle between the direction of the force and the direction of motion.

Assuming, in (2.43), that $k = 1$, $F = 1$ pdl, $s = 1$ ft, and $\alpha = 0°$, we get:

1 unit of work $= 1 \cdot 1$ pdl $\cdot 1$ ft $\cdot 1 = 1$ ft $\cdot$ pdl

This unit of work is called the foot-poundal (ft-pdl).

The ft-pdl is the work done by a constant force of 1 pdl acting on a body over a distance of 1 ft in the direction of the force.

The dimensions of the unit of work in the f lbm s system are:

$$[W] = [F][s] = \text{ft} \cdot \text{lbm} \cdot \text{sec}^{-2} \cdot \text{ft} = \text{ft}^2 \cdot \text{lbm} \cdot \text{sec}^{-2}$$

As in the MKS system (cf. Section 1 of this chapter), the unit of work can also be determined from the kinetic energy equation for forward motion (K.E. $= k \dfrac{m \cdot v^2}{2}$), or from the potential energy equation for a raised body (P.E. $= kmg \cdot H$), or, finally, from the potential energy equation for a deformed body (P.E. $= k \dfrac{k' (\Delta L)^2}{2}$).

Power. The unit of power P is determined from the equation:

$$P = k \frac{W}{t} \qquad (2.44)$$

where W is the work done in time t.

Assuming, in this formula, that $k = 1$, $W = 1$ ft-pdl, and $t = 1$ sec, we find that:

$$1 \text{ unit of power} = 1 \times \frac{1 \text{ ft-pdl}}{1 \text{ sec}} = 1 \frac{\text{ft-pdl}}{\text{sec}}$$

This unit is called the foot-poundal per second.

The foot-poundal per second is the power at which 1 pdl of work is done in 1 sec.

The dimensions of the unit of power are:

$$[p] = \frac{[W]}{[t]} = \frac{\text{ft}^2 \cdot \text{lbm} \cdot \text{sec}^{-2}}{\text{sec}} = \text{ft}^2 \cdot \text{lbm} \cdot \text{sec}^{-3}$$

Torque (moment of force). The fundamental equation for the torque M is:

$$M = kF \cdot r \qquad (2.45)$$

where F is the force and r is the arm of the force F, that is, the shortest distance between the axis of rotation and the direction of the force.

Assuming, in Eq. (2.45), that $k = 1$, $F = 1$ pdl, and $r = 1$ ft, we find that:

$$1 \text{ unit of torque} = 1 \text{ pdl} \cdot 1 \text{ ft} = 1 \text{ ft} \cdot \text{pdl}$$

In the f lbm s system, the unit of torque is taken as the torque exerted by 1 pdl with an arm equal to 1 ft.

The dimensions of the unit of torque are:

$$[M] = [F][r] = \text{ft} \cdot \text{lbm} \cdot \text{sec}^{-2} \cdot \text{ft} = \text{ft}^2 \cdot \text{lbm} \cdot \text{sec}^{-2}$$

From Eqs. (2.43) and (2.45), we can see that work and torque have the same dimensions.

Torque impulse. The unit of measurement for the torque impulse is found from the fundamental equation:

$$L = kM \cdot t \qquad (2.46)$$

where M is the torque and t is the time over which the torque acts.

Setting $k = 1$, $M = 1$ ft $\cdot$ pdl, and $t = 1$ sec, we find that:

$$1 \text{ unit of torque impulse} = 1 \text{ pdl} \cdot \text{ft} \cdot 1 \text{ sec} = 1 \text{ ft} \cdot \text{pdl} \cdot \text{sec}$$

The unit of torque impulse, in the f lbm s system, is taken as the torque impulse exerted by a torque of 1 ft $\cdot$ pdl acting for 1 sec.

The dimensions of the unit of torque impulse are:

$$[L] = [M][t] = \text{ft}^2 \cdot \text{lbm} \cdot \text{sec}^{-2} \cdot \text{sec} = \text{ft}^2 \cdot \text{lbm} \cdot \text{sec}^{-1}$$

Moment of inertia. The unit of moment of inertia is found from the equation:

$$I = km \cdot r^2 \qquad (2.47)$$

where m is the mass of a particle and r is the distance between the particle and the rotation axis.

Assuming, in Eq. (2.47), that $k = 1$, $m = 1$ lbm, and $r = 1$ ft, we find that:

$$1 \text{ unit of moment of inertia} = 1 \cdot 1 \text{ lbm} \cdot 1 \text{ ft}^2 = 1 \text{ lbm} \cdot \text{ft}^2$$

In the f lbm s system, the unit of moment of inertia is taken as the moment of inertia possessed by a rotating particle with a mass of 1 lbm at a distance of 1 ft from the rotation axis.

The dimensions of the unit of moment of inertia are:

$$[I] = [m][r^2] = \text{lbm} \cdot \text{ft}^2 = \text{ft}^2 \cdot \text{lbm}$$

The units of frequency, angular velocity, and angular acceleration are the same as in the MKS system (cf. Section 1 of this chapter).

The unit of frequency is 1/sec, and its dimensions are sec^{-1}.

The unit of angular velocity is rad/sec, and its dimensions are sec^{-1}. Angular velocity may also be measured in rps or rpm.

The unit of angular acceleration is rad/sec², and its dimensions are sec^{-2}. Angular acceleration may also be measured in rps² or rpm² (cf. Section 7 of this chapter).

Angular momentum. The unit of measurement of angular momentum L is determined from the equation:

$$L = k \cdot I \cdot \omega \qquad (2.48)$$

where I is the moment of inertia of the body and ω is its angular velocity.

Assuming that $k = 1$, $I = 1$ lbm · ft², and $\omega = 1$ rad/sec, we find that:

$$1 \text{ unit of angular momentum} =$$
$$1 \cdot 1 \text{ lbm} \cdot \text{ft}^2 \cdot 1 \frac{\text{rad}}{\text{sec}} = 1 \frac{\text{lbm} \cdot \text{ft}^2 \cdot \text{rad}}{\text{sec}}$$

The unit of angular momentum in the f lbm s system is taken as the angular momentum of a body with a moment of inertia of 1 lbm · ft² with respect to the axis about which it rotates uniformly at an angular velocity of 1 rad/sec.

The dimensions of angular momentum are:

$$[L] = [I][\omega] = \text{ft}^2 \cdot \text{lbm} \cdot \text{sec}^{-1}$$

5. THE BRITISH GRAVITATIONAL (F LBF S) SYSTEM

The British gravitational system is analogous to the MKGFS system (cf. Section 3 of this chapter) in that its fundamental quantities are length, force, and time. Mass, in the f lbf s system, is a derived quantity, not a fundamental one as in the f lbm s system considered above.

Like the other systems, the f lbf s system derives its name from its fundamental units.

The British gravitational (f lbf s) system is most commonly used in engineering, and is not used in electricity, magnetism, and certain other branches of physics.

1. FUNDAMENTAL UNITS IN THE
F LBF S SYSTEM

The fundamental units in the f lbf s system are:

The foot (ft)—the unit of length (defined in Section 4).

The pound-force (lbf)—the unit of force.

The pound-force (lbf) is the force due to gravity exerted by a body with a mass of 1 lbm at a location where the acceleration of gravity (g) equals 32.174 ft per sec² (in other words, the weight of a mass of 1 lbm).

The second (sec)—the unit of time (defined earlier).

2. DERIVED UNITS IN THE F LBF S SYSTEM

In the formulation of the f lbf s system, the arrangement of the fundamental equations differs slightly from the arrangement adopted for the f lbm s system. In the f lbf s system, Newton's second law is the fundamental equation for mass, rather than for force.

The dimensions of most of the physical quantities and the units for their measurement are also expressed in an essentially different manner (the units differ in principle).

The f lbf s system is often confused with the f lbm s system, since the units of length (ft), velocity (ft/sec), acceleration (ft/sec²), and certain other quantities are the same for both. Furthermore, historically, the unit of mass in the f lbm s system and the unit of force in the f lbf s system have come to be known by the same name—the pound. This fact is the cause of frequent misunderstanding in solving physical problems. It should, therefore, be kept firmly in mind that the lbm is a unit of mass in the f lbm s system, whereas the lbf is a unit of force in the f lbf s system.

The order of the fundamental equations adopted in the f lbf s system is shown in Table 5.

Using these fundamental equations, we can find the derived units of the f lbf s system. We will only derive those units which differ in dimensions from the corresponding units in the f lbm s system.

Mass. The unit of mass m can be obtained from Newton's second law:

$$F = kma$$

From which

$$m = \frac{1}{k}\frac{F}{a} \qquad (2.49)$$

Setting $k = 1$, $F = 1$ lbf, and $a = 1$ ft/sec², we find that:

$$1 \text{ unit of mass} = 1 \times \frac{1 \text{ lbf}}{1\frac{\text{ft}}{\text{sec}^2}} = 1\frac{\text{lbf} \cdot \text{sec}^2}{\text{ft}}$$

Table 5

Units of Measurement of Mechanical Quantities in the f lbf s System

Quantity	Fundamental equation	Unit of measurement		
		Name of unit	Abbreviation	Dimensions
Velocity	$v = \dfrac{s}{t}$	—	$\dfrac{\text{ft}}{\text{sec}}$	ft · sec⁻¹
Acceleration	$a = \dfrac{v}{t}$	—	$\dfrac{\text{ft}}{\text{sec}^2}$	ft · sec⁻²
Mass	$m = \dfrac{F}{a}$	slug	$\dfrac{\text{lbf} \cdot \text{sec}^2}{\text{ft}}$	ft⁻¹ · lbf · sec²
Pressure (stress)	$p = \dfrac{F}{S}$	—	$\dfrac{\text{lbf}}{\text{ft}^2}$	ft⁻² · lbf
Specific weight	$d = \dfrac{w}{V}$	—	$\dfrac{\text{lbf}}{\text{ft}^3}$	ft⁻³ · lbf
Density	$\rho = \dfrac{m}{V}$	—	$\dfrac{\text{slug}}{\text{ft}^3}$	ft⁻⁴ · lbf · sec²
Specific volume	$V_0 = \dfrac{V}{m}$	—	$\dfrac{\text{ft}^3}{\text{slug}}$	ft⁴ · lbf⁻¹ · sec⁻²
Impulse	$k = F \cdot t$	—	lbf-sec	lbf · sec
Momentum	$K = m \cdot v$	—	lbf-sec	lbf · sec
Work (energy)	$W = F \cdot s$	foot-pound	ft-lbf	ft · lbf
Power	$P = \dfrac{W}{t}$	—	$\dfrac{\text{ft-lbf}}{\text{sec}}$	ft · lbf · sec⁻¹
Torque	$M = F \cdot r$	—	—	ft · lbf
Torque impulse	$L = M \cdot t$	—	—	ft · lbf · sec
Moment of inertia	$I = m \cdot r^2$	—	—	ft · lbf · sec²
Frequency	$f = \dfrac{1}{T}$	cycle per sec	cps	sec⁻¹
Angular velocity	$\omega = \dfrac{\varphi}{t}$	radian per sec	$\dfrac{\text{rad}}{\text{sec}}$	sec⁻¹
Angular acceleration	$\epsilon = \dfrac{\omega}{t}$	—	$\dfrac{\text{rad}}{\text{sec}^2}$	sec⁻²
Angular momentum	$L = I \cdot \omega$	—	—	ft · lbf · sec

This unit is called the *slug*.

The slug is the mass to which a force of 1 lbf imparts an acceleration of 1 ft/sec².

The dimensions of this unit are ft⁻¹ · lbf · sec².

Pressure. The unit of pressure p is determined from the equation:

$$p = k \frac{F}{S} \qquad (2.50)$$

Setting $k = 1$, $F = 1$ lbf, and $S = 1$ ft^2, we find that:

$$1 \text{ unit of pressure } = 1 \times \frac{1 \text{ lbf}}{1 \text{ ft}^2} = 1 \frac{\text{lbf}}{\text{ft}^2}$$

The unit of pressure in the f lbf s system is the uniform pressure exerted by a force of 1 lbf over an area of 1 ft^2.

As follows from Eq. (2.50), the dimensions of this unit are ft$^{-2}\cdot$lbf.

Specific weight. The fundamental equation for the unit of specific weight d is

$$d = k \frac{w}{V} \qquad (2.51)$$

where w is the weight of a homogeneous body occupying the volume V.

Assuming, in (2.51), that $k = 1$, $w = 1$ lbf, and $V = 1$ ft^3, we find that:

$$1 \text{ unit of specific weight } = 1 \times \frac{1 \text{ lbf}}{1 \text{ ft}^3} = 1 \frac{\text{lbf}}{\text{ft}^3}$$

In the f lbf s system, the unit of specific weight is the specific weight of a homogeneous body, 1 ft^3 of which weighs 1 lbf.

The dimensions of the unit of specific weight are ft$^{-3} \cdot$ lbf.

Density. The unit of density ρ in the f lbf s system is determined by the equation:

$$\rho = k \frac{m}{V} \qquad (2.52)$$

Setting $k = 1$, $m = 1$ slug, and $V = 1$ ft^3, we find that:

$$1 \text{ unit of density } = 1 \times \frac{1 \text{ slug}}{1 \text{ ft}^3} = 1 \frac{\text{slug}}{\text{ft}^3}$$

In the f lbf s system the unit of density is the density of a homogeneous substance, 1 slug of which occupies 1 ft^3.

The dimensions of the unit of density are:

$$[\rho] = \frac{[m]}{[V]} = \text{ft}^{-1} \cdot \text{lbf} \cdot \text{sec}^2 \cdot \text{ft}^{-3} = \text{ft}^{-4} \cdot \text{lbf} \cdot \text{sec}^2$$

Specific volume. The unit of specific volume V_0 is determined from the equation:

$$V_0 = k\,\frac{V}{m} \tag{2.53}$$

Setting $k = 1$, $V = 1$ ft^3, and $m = 1$ slug, we find that:

$$1 \text{ unit of specific volume } = 1 \times \frac{1 \text{ ft}^3}{1 \text{ slug}} = 1\,\frac{\text{ft}^3}{\text{slug}}$$

In the f lbf s system, the unit of specific volume is the specific volume of a homogeneous substance, 1 slug of which occupies a volume of 1 ft^3.

It follows from Eq. (2.53) that the dimensions of the unit of specific volume are:

$$[V_0] = \frac{[V]}{[m]} = \frac{\text{ft}^3}{\text{ft}^{-1} \cdot \text{lbf} \cdot \text{sec}^2} = \text{ft}^4 \cdot \text{lbf}^{-1} \cdot \text{sec}^{-2}$$

Impulse. The fundamental equation for the unit of impulse K is the following:

$$K = kF \cdot \Delta t \tag{2.54}$$

Setting $k = 1$, $F = 1$ lbf, and $\Delta t = 1$ sec, we find that:

$$1 \text{ unit of impulse } = 1 \cdot 1 \text{ lbf} \cdot 1 \text{ sec } = 1 \text{ lbf} \cdot \text{sec}$$

In the f lbf s system, the unit of impulse is the impulse created by a force of 1 lbf acting for 1 sec.

As follows from Eq. (2.54), the dimensions of the unit of impulse in the f lbf s system are lbf $\cdot$ sec.

The dimensions of the unit of momentum are also lbf $\cdot$ sec. This follows from the well-known equation in mechanics:

$$F \Delta t = \Delta (mv)$$

Work (energy). The unit of measurement of work W can be determined from the equation:

$$W = kF \cdot s \cdot \cos \alpha \tag{2.55}$$

Assuming, in this formula, that $k = 1$, $F = 1$ lbf, $s = 1$ ft, and $\alpha = 0°$, we find that:

$$1 \text{ unit of work } = 1 \cdot 1 \text{ lbf} \cdot 1 \text{ ft} \cdot 1 = 1 \text{ lbf} \cdot \text{ft}$$

In the f lbf s system, the unit of work is called the foot-pound.

The foot-pound (ft-lbf) is the work done by a constant force of 1 lbf acting over a distance of 1 ft (and in the same direction as the displacement).

The dimensions of the foot-pound are determined from Eq. (2.55):

$$[W] = [F][s] = \text{lbf} \cdot \text{ft} = \text{ft} \cdot \text{lbf}$$

Power. The unit of power P is determined from the equation:

$$P = k\frac{W}{t} \qquad (2.56)$$

Setting $k = 1$, $W = 1$ ft-lbf, and $t = 1$ sec, we find that:

$$1 \text{ unit of power} = 1 \times \frac{1 \text{ ft-lbf}}{1 \text{ sec}} = 1\frac{\text{ft-lbf}}{\text{sec}}$$

In the f lbf s system, the unit of power is the power at which 1 ft-lbf of work is done in 1 sec.

The horsepower is also a commonly used unit of power in the f lbf s system. It is defined as 550 ft-lbf/sec.

It follows from Eq. (2.56) that the dimensions of the unit of power in the f lbf s system are ft $\cdot$ lbf $\cdot$ sec $^{-1}$.

Torque (moment of force). The fundamental equation of the unit of torque M is:

$$M = kF \cdot r \qquad (2.57)$$

Setting $k = 1$, $F = 1$ lbf, and $r = 1$ ft, we find that:

$$1 \text{ unit of torque} = 1 \cdot 1 \text{ lbf} \cdot 1 \text{ ft} = 1 \text{ ft} \cdot \text{lbf}$$

In the f lbf s system, the unit of torque is taken as the torque exerted by a force of 1 lbf with an arm of 1 ft.

The dimensions of the unit of torque are the same as those of the unit of work—ft $\cdot$ lbf.

Torque impulse. The unit of torque impulse L can be determined from the equation:

$$L = kM \cdot t \qquad (2.58)$$

Assuming, in this formula, that $k = 1$, $M = 1$ ft-lbf, and $t = 1$ sec, we find that:

$$1 \text{ unit of torque impulse} = 1 \cdot 1 \text{ ft-lbf} \cdot 1 \text{ sec} = 1 \text{ ft-lbf} \cdot \text{sec}$$

The unit of torque impulse in the f lbf s system is the torque impulse exerted by a torque of 1 ft-lbf acting for 1 sec.

The dimensions of torque impulse are found from Eq. (2.58):

$$[L] = [M][t] = \text{ft-lbf} \cdot \text{sec}$$

Moment of inertia. The fundamental equation for the moment of inertia is as follows:

$$I = km \cdot r^2 \qquad (2.59)$$

Setting $k = 1$, $m = 1$ slug, and $r = 1$ ft, we find that:

1 unit of moment of inertia = $1 \cdot 1$ slug $\cdot 1$ ft^2 = 1 slug $\cdot$ ft^2

In the f lbf s system, the unit of moment of inertia is the moment of inertia possessed by a rotating particle of mass 1 slug at a distance 1 ft from the rotation axis.

The dimensions of the unit of moment of inertia are found from Eq. (2.59):

$$[I] = [m][r^2] = \text{ft}^{-1} \cdot \text{lbf} \cdot \text{sec}^2 \cdot \text{ft}^2 = \text{ft} \cdot \text{lbf} \cdot \text{sec}^2$$

Angular momentum. The unit of angular momentum L is determined from the equation:

$$L = kI\omega \qquad (2.60)$$

Setting $k = 1$, $I = 1$ ft $\cdot$ lbf $\cdot$ sec^2, and $\omega = 1$ rad/sec, we find that:

1 unit of angular momentum
$$= 1 \cdot 1 \text{ ft} \cdot \text{lbf} \cdot \text{sec}^2 \cdot 1 \frac{\text{rad}}{\text{sec}} = 1 \text{ ft} \cdot \text{lbf} \cdot \text{sec} \cdot \text{rad}$$

The unit of angular momentum in the f lbf s system is taken as the angular momentum possessed by a body with a moment of inertia of 1 ft-lbf $\cdot$ sec^2 with respect to the axis about which it rotates at an angular velocity of 1 rad/sec.

The dimensions of the unit of angular momentum in the f lbf s system are ft $\cdot$ lbf $\cdot$ sec $\cdot$ rad or, if we leave out the angle, as is often done, ft $\cdot$ lbf $\cdot$ sec.

6. RELATIONSHIPS AMONG MECHANICAL UNITS
IN DIFFERENT SYSTEMS

When solving physics problems, we often need to convert the numerical values of a physical quantity from one system of units to another.

Let us develop a method of deriving relationships between the units of similar mechanical quantities in different systems.

In order to express a derived unit in one system (A) in the units of another system (B), we have to carry out the following operations:

(a) note the dimensions of the derived unit;

(b) express these dimensions (fundamental units of the system A) in terms of the corresponding units in the system B (it is assumed that the relationship between the fundamental units in A and the corresponding units in B is known);*

(c) carry out the algebraic operations in the expression, using the conversion factors as well as the names of the fundamental units in system B.

Let us determine the relationship between units in the MKS, cgs, f lbm s, and f lbf s systems on the basis of these rules.

1. RELATIONSHIPS AMONG UNITS IN MKS AND CGS SYSTEMS

In accordance with (b) above, we must first establish the relationship between the fundamental units in the MKS system (m, kg) and the corresponding units in the cgs system (cm, g).

These relationships are known from the metric system of measurement and are expressed by the equalities:

$$1 \text{ m} = 100 \text{ cm}$$
$$1 \text{ kg} = 10^3 \text{ g}$$

Relationship between units of area—m^2 and cm^2. The unit of area in the MKS system is 1 m^2. Expressing m (in the dimension of this unit) in terms of cm, we find:

$$1 \text{ m}^2 = 1 \cdot (100 \text{ cm})^2$$

Hence:

$$1 \text{ m}^2 = 10^4 \text{ cm}^2$$
$$1 \text{ cm}^2 = 10^{-4} \text{ m}^2$$

Relationship between units of volume—m^3 and cm^3. The unit of volume in the MKS system is 1 m^3. Expressing m in terms of cm, we find:

$$1 \text{ m}^3 = 1 \cdot (100 \text{ cm})^3$$

from which:

$$1 \text{ m}^3 = 10^6 \text{ cm}^3$$
$$1 \text{ cm}^3 = 10^{-6} \text{ m}^3$$

---

* Note. In cases where the derived unit to be converted (in system A) can be expressed in terms of other derived units in the same system, and where the relationship between these latter derived units and the corresponding units in B is known, it is not necessary to use the dimensions of the units. In such cases, we need only express the unit to be converted in terms of derived units in the same system, then express the latter in terms of the corresponding units in B, and finally carry out the indicated algebraic operations.

Relationship between units of force—newton and dyne. In accordance with paragraph (a) of the rules, let us write down the dimensions of the unit of force in the MKS system, the newton:

$$1 \text{ N} = 1 \frac{\text{kg} \cdot \text{m}}{\text{sec}^2}$$

These dimensions can be found in Table 1 or can be derived using the fundamental equation for the unit of force:

$$F = m \cdot a$$

Next, in accordance with (b) of the rules, let us express kg and m in terms of g and cm, respectively. This gives us:

$$1 \text{ N} = 1 \times \frac{(10^3\text{g}) \cdot (100 \text{ cm})}{\text{sec}^2}$$

Finally, carrying out the algebraic operations with the numbers and names of the units in accordance with paragraph (c), we obtain:

$$1 \text{ N} = 10^5 \frac{\text{g} \cdot \text{cm}}{\text{sec}^2}$$

But $\dfrac{\text{g} \cdot \text{cm}}{\text{sec}^2}$ are the dimensions of the unit of force in the cgs system, the dyne. Consequently,

$$1 \text{ N} = 10^5 \text{ dynes}$$
$$1 \text{ dyne} = 10^{-5} \text{ N}$$

Relationship between units of work—joule and erg. In order to determine the relationship between the unit of work in the MKS system (joule) and the unit of work in the cgs system (erg), we must first determine the dimensions of the joule by finding them in Table 1 or by using the fundamental equation:

$$W = Fs$$

Then we write down the equality:

$$1 \text{ J} = 1 \frac{\text{kg} \cdot \text{m}^2}{\text{sec}^2}$$

Finally, expressing the fundamental units of the MKS system, kg and m, in terms of g and cm, respectively, we obtain:

$$1 \text{ J} = 1 \times \frac{10^3\text{g} \cdot (100 \text{ cm})^2}{\text{sec}^2}$$

or:

$$1 \text{ J} = 10^7 \frac{\text{g} \cdot \text{cm}^2}{\text{sec}^2} = 10^7 \text{ ergs}$$

This gives us equations expressing the relationship between the joule and the erg:

$$1 \text{ J} = 10^7 \text{ erg}$$
$$1 \text{ erg} = 10^{-7} \text{ J}$$

It is simpler, however, to establish the relationship between the joule and the erg without resorting to dimensions (see footnote on page 45).

By definition:

$$1 \text{ J} = 1 \text{ N} \cdot 1 \text{ m}$$

Since the relationship between the newton and the dyne has already been established above, we can express N in dynes and m in cm on the right-hand side of this equality, obtaining:

$$1 \text{ J} = 10^5 \text{ dynes} \cdot 100 \text{ cm} = 10^7 \text{ dyne} \cdot \text{cm}$$
$$1 \text{ J} = 10^7 \text{ ergs}$$

From now on, when establishing the relationship between units in different systems, wherever possible we will use the simpler method, and not resort to the dimensions of the unit.

Relationship between units of power—watt and erg/sec. The fundamental equation of power:

$$P = \frac{W}{t}$$

gives us:

$$1 \text{ watt} = 1 \frac{1 \text{ J}}{1 \text{ sec}}$$

Expressing J in ergs in the right-hand side of this equality, we obtain:

$$1 \text{ watt} = \frac{10^7 \text{ ergs}}{1 \text{ sec}} = 10^7 \frac{\text{erg}}{\text{sec}}$$

from which:

$$1 \text{ watt} = 10^7 \frac{\text{erg}}{\text{sec}}$$

$$1 \frac{erg}{sec} = 10^{-7} \text{ watt}$$

Relationship between units of pressure—newton/m² and barye.
From the fundamental equation for pressure:

$$p = \frac{F}{S}$$

we determine the unit of pressure in the MKS system, N/m^2.
Expressing N in dynes and m in cm, we obtain:

$$1 \frac{N}{m^2} = \frac{10^5 \text{ dynes}}{(100 \text{ cm})^2} = 10 \frac{\text{dyne}}{cm^2}$$

But, by definition, 1 dyne/cm² = 1 barye; therefore:

$$1 \frac{N}{m^2} = 10 \text{ baryes}$$

$$1 \text{ barye} = 0.1 \frac{N}{m^2}$$

Relationship between units of density—kg/m³ and g/cm³. From
the fundamental equation for density:

$$\rho = \frac{m}{V}$$

we find that the unit of density in the MKS system is kg/m^3. Expressing kg and m in terms of g and cm, respectively, we obtain:

$$1 \frac{kg}{m^3} = \frac{10^3 g}{(100 \text{ cm})^3}$$

Carrying out the algebraic operations, we derive the relationship
between the units of density.

$$1 \frac{kg}{m^3} = 10^{-3} \frac{g}{cm^3}$$

$$1 \frac{g}{cm^3} = 10^3 \frac{kg}{m^3}$$

Relationship between units of specific weight—N/m³ and dyne/cm³.
The fundamental equation for specific weight $d = w/V$ gives us the
unit of specific weight in the MKS system—N/m^3.

Expressing N and m in terms of dynes and cm, respectively, we obtain:

$$1\,\frac{N}{m^3} = 1 \times \frac{10^5 \text{ dynes}}{(100 \text{ cm})^3}$$

Carrying out the algebraic operations, we find:

$$1\,\frac{N}{m^3} = 0.1\,\frac{dyne}{cm^3}$$

$$1\,\frac{dyne}{cm^3} = 10\,\frac{N}{m^3}$$

Relationship between units of moment of inertia—kg · m² and g · cm². From the fundamental equation for moment of inertia:

$$I = m \cdot r^2$$

we find that the dimensions of the moment of inertia in the MKS system are m² · kg. Expressing kg and m in terms of g and cm, respectively, we obtain:

$$1 \text{ m}^2 \cdot \text{kg} = 1 \cdot (100 \text{ cm})^2 \cdot 10^3 \text{g}$$

from which:

$$1 \text{ kg} \cdot \text{m}^2 = 10^7 \text{ g} \cdot \text{cm}^2$$
$$1 \text{ g} \cdot \text{cm}^2 = 10^{-7} \text{ kg} \cdot \text{m}^2$$

We can find the relationship between the units of measurement in the MKS and cgs systems for other mechanical quantities in a similar fashion.

2. RELATIONSHIPS AMONG UNITS IN THE MKS AND F LBM S SYSTEMS

In accordance with (b) of the rules, we must first establish the relationship between the fundamental units in the MKS system (m, kg) and the corresponding units in the f lbm s system (ft, lbm).

These relationships can be obtained from the definitions of the foot and the pound:

$$1 \text{ m} = 3.28 \text{ ft}$$
$$1 \text{ kg} = 2.205 \text{ lbm}$$

Relationship between units of area—m² and ft². The unit of area in the MKS system is 1 m². Expressing m (in the dimension of this unit) in terms of ft, we find:

$$1 \text{ m}^2 = 1 \cdot (3.28 \text{ ft})^2$$

Hence:

$$1 \text{ m}^2 = 10.76 \text{ ft}^2$$
$$1 \text{ ft}^2 = 0.093 \text{ m}^2$$

Relationship between units of volume—m^3 and ft^2. The unit of volume in the MKS system is 1 m³. Expressing m in terms of ft, we find:

$$1 \text{ m}^3 = 1 \cdot (3.28 \text{ ft})^3$$

from which:

$$1 \text{ m}^3 = 35.3 \text{ ft}^3$$
$$1 \text{ ft}^3 = 0.0283 \text{ m}^3$$

Relationship between units of force—newton and poundal. In accordance with paragraph (a) of the rules for converting units, let us write down the dimensions of the unit of force in the MKS system, the newton:

$$1 \text{ N} = 1 \frac{\text{kg} \cdot \text{m}}{\text{sec}^2}$$

Next, in accordance with (b) of the rules, let us express kg and m in terms of lbm and ft, respectively. This gives us:

$$1 \text{ N} = 1 \times \frac{(2.205 \text{ lbm}) \cdot (3.28 \text{ ft})}{\text{sec}^2}$$

Finally, carrying out the algebraic operations with the numbers and the names of the units, in accordance with paragraph (c), we find:

$$1 \text{ N} = 7.23 \frac{\text{lbm} \cdot \text{ft}}{\text{sec}^2}$$

But $\dfrac{\text{lbm} \cdot \text{ft}}{\text{sec}^2}$ are the dimensions of the unit of force in the f lbm s system, the poundal. Consequently:

$$1 \text{ N} = 7.23 \text{ pdl}$$
$$1 \text{ pdl} = 0.138 \text{ N}$$

Relationship between units of work—joule and foot-poundal. In order to determine the relationship between the joule and the foot-poundal, we must first note the dimensions of the joule:

$$1 \text{ J} = 1 \frac{\text{kg} \cdot \text{m}^2}{\text{sec}^2}$$

Then we express the fundamental units of the MKS system, kg and m, in terms of lbm and ft, respectively, obtaining:

$$1 \text{ J} = 1 \times \frac{(2.205 \text{ lbm}) \cdot (3.28 \text{ ft})^2}{\text{sec}^2}$$

or:

$$1 \text{ J} = 23.7 \frac{\text{lbm} \cdot \text{ft}^2}{\text{sec}^2} = 23.7 \text{ ft-pdl}$$

$$1 \text{ ft-pdl} = 4.21 \cdot 10^{-2} \text{ J}$$

It is simpler, however, to establish the relationship between the joule and the foot-poundal without resorting to dimensions (see footnote on page 45).

By definition:

$$1 \text{ J} = 1 \text{ N} \cdot 1 \text{ m}$$

Since the relationship between the newton and the poundal has already been established above, we can express N in poundals and m in ft on the right-hand side of this equality. Then,

$$1 \text{ J} = 1 \ (7.23 \text{ pdl})(3.28 \text{ ft}) = 23.7 \text{ ft-pdl}$$

From now on, when establishing the relationship between units in different systems, wherever possible we will use the simpler method and not resort to the dimensions of the unit.

Relationship between units of power—watt and foot-poundal/sec. The fundamental equation of power:

$$P = \frac{W}{t}$$

gives us:

$$1 \text{ watt} = 1 \frac{1 \text{ J}}{1 \text{ sec}} = 1 \times \frac{23.7 \text{ ft-pdl}}{1 \text{ sec}} = 23.7 \frac{\text{ft-pdl}}{\text{sec}}$$

$$1 \frac{\text{ft-pdl}}{\text{sec}} = 4.21 \cdot 10^{-2} \text{ watt}$$

Relationship between units of pressure—newton/m² and pdl/ft². The fundamental equation for pressure is:

$$p = \frac{F}{S}$$

Thus, the unit of pressure in the MKS system is N/m^2. Expressing N in poundals and m in ft, we obtain:

$$1 \frac{N}{m^2} = \frac{7.23 \text{ pdl}}{(3.28 \text{ ft})^2} = 0.672 \frac{\text{pdl}}{\text{ft}^2}$$

$$1 \frac{\text{pdl}}{\text{ft}^2} = 1.49 \frac{N}{m^2}$$

Relationship between units of density—kg/m^3 and lbm/ft^3. From the fundamental equation for density:

$$\rho = \frac{m}{V}$$

we find that the unit of density in the MKS system is kg/m^3. Expressing kg and m in terms of lbm and ft, we find:

$$1 \frac{kg}{m^3} = \frac{2.205 \text{ lbm}}{(3.28 \text{ ft})^3} = 0.062 \frac{\text{lbm}}{\text{ft}^3}$$

$$1 \frac{\text{lbm}}{\text{ft}^3} = 16.0 \frac{kg}{m^3}$$

Relationship between units of specific weight—N/m^3 and pdl/ft^3. The fundamental equation for specific weight $d = w/V$ gives us the unit of specific weight in the MKS system—N/m^3.

Expressing N and m in terms of poundals and ft, respectively, we obtain:

$$1 \frac{N}{m^3} = 1 \times \frac{7.23 \text{ pdl}}{(3.28 \text{ ft})^3} = 0.205 \frac{\text{pdl}}{\text{ft}^3}$$

$$1 \frac{\text{pdl}}{\text{ft}^3} = 4.88 \frac{N}{m^3}$$

Relationship between units of moment of inertia—$kg \cdot m^2$ and $lbm \cdot ft^2$. From the fundamental equation for moment of inertia $I = mr^2$, we find that the dimensions of the moment of inertia in the MKS system are $m^2 \cdot kg$. Expressing kg and m in terms of lbm and ft, respectively, we obtain:

$$1 \text{ kg} \cdot m^2 = 1 \cdot (2.205 \text{ lbm}) \cdot (3.28 \text{ ft})^2 = 23.7 \text{ lbm} \cdot \text{ft}^2$$
$$1 \text{ lbm} \cdot \text{ft}^2 = 0.042 \text{ kg} \cdot m^2$$

We can find the relationship between the units of measurement for the mechanical quantities in the MKS and f lbm s systems in a similar fashion.

3. OTHER UNITS IN THE F LBM S AND F LBF S SYSTEMS

The following units of length are common to both the British absolute and British gravitational systems:

$$1 \text{ ft} = 12 \text{ inches (in)}$$
$$1 \text{ yard (yd)} = 3 \text{ ft}$$
$$1 \text{ mile (mi)} = 5280 \text{ ft}$$

Using the methods developed in previous sections we can obtain the following results for both the f lbm s and f lbf s systems.

Area:
$$1 \text{ ft} = 1 \cdot (12 \text{ in})^2 = 144 \text{ in}^2$$
$$1 \text{ in}^2 = \frac{1}{144} \text{ ft}^2 = \frac{1}{144}(0.093 \text{ m}^2) = 6.45 \cdot 10^{-4} \text{ m}^2$$
$$1 \text{ yd}^2 = 9 \text{ ft}^2 = 9 \cdot (0.093 \text{ m}^2) = 0.837 \text{ m}^2$$
$$1 \text{ mi}^2 = 1 \cdot (5280 \text{ ft})^2 = 2.79 \cdot 10^7 \text{ ft}^2 =$$
$$2.79 \cdot 10^7 (0.093 \text{ m}^2) = 2.59 \cdot 10^6 \text{ m}^2$$

Volume:
$$1 \text{ ft}^3 = 1 \cdot (12 \text{ in})^3 = 1728 \text{ in}^3$$
$$1 \text{ in}^3 = \frac{1}{1728} \text{ ft}^3 = \frac{1}{1728}(0.0283 \text{ m}^3) = 1.64 \cdot 10^{-5} \text{ m}^3$$
$$1 \text{ yd}^3 = 27 \text{ ft}^3 = 27 \cdot (0.0283 \text{ m}^3) = 0.765 \text{ m}^3$$

Another unit of volume in the f lbm s and f lbf s systems is the gallon (U.S.):

$$1 \text{ gallon} = 0.133 \text{ ft}^3$$
$$= 0.133 \cdot (1728 \text{ in}^3) = 231 \text{ in}^3.$$

Velocity:

(We note here that 1 hr = 3600 sec.)

$$1 \frac{\text{mi}}{\text{hr}} = 1 \times \frac{5280 \text{ ft}}{3600 \text{ sec}} = \frac{22}{15} \frac{\text{ft}}{\text{sec}}$$

$$1 \frac{\text{ft}}{\text{sec}} = \frac{15}{22} \frac{\text{mi}}{\text{hr}}$$

These quantities can be related to the cgs system using the results of Subsection 1 and the methods already familiar to us. They can, similarly, be applied to results to be obtained in subsequent sections.

4. RELATIONSHIPS AMONG UNITS IN THE
F LBM S AND F LBF S SYSTEMS

The relationship between units of force—poundal (pdl) and pound-weight (lbf). We recall that:

(a) when a force of 1 pdl acts on a body of mass 1 lbm, it imparts to it an acceleration of 1 ft/sec^2;

(b) the same body, when acted on by its own weight (equal to 1 lbf) develops an acceleration during free fall of 32.174 ft/sec^2.

Let us note the above facts in the following form:

1 pdl acting on a body of mass 1 lbm imparts to it an acceleration of 1 ft/sec^2;

1 lbf acting on a body of mass 1 lbm imparts to it an acceleration of 32.174 ft/sec^2.

Thus, the acceleration imparted by a force of 1 lbf is 32.174 times greater than the acceleration imparted to the same mass by a force of 1 pdl. Consequently, a force of 1 lbf is 32.174 times greater than a force of 1 pdl, that is:

$$1 \text{ lbf} = 32.174 \text{ pdl}$$
$$1 \text{ pdl} = 0.031 \text{ lbf}$$

Relationship between units of mass—lbm and slug. The relationship between pdl and lbf suggests the following:

To impart an acceleration of 1 ft/sec^2 to a mass of 1 lbm, we require a force of 1 pdl; to impart the same acceleration to a mass of 1 slug, we require a force of 1 lbf = 32.174 pdl.

Hence, in order to impart a given acceleration to a mass of 1 slug, we require a force 32.174 times greater than would be required to impart the same acceleration to a mass of 1 lbm. Consequently, 1 lbm is 32.174 times smaller than 1 slug, that is:

$$1 \text{ lbm} = \frac{1}{32.174} \text{ slug} = 0.031 \text{ slug}$$
$$1 \text{ slug} = 32.174 \text{ lbm}$$

Relationship between units of work—foot-poundal and foot-pound-weight (ft-pdl and ft-lbf). Applying the fundamental equation for work $(W = F \cdot s)$, we find:

$$1 \text{ ft-pdl} = 1 \text{ pdl} \cdot 1 \text{ ft}$$
$$= 0.031 \text{ lbf} \cdot 1 \text{ ft} = 0.031 \text{ ft-lbf}$$
$$1 \text{ ft-lbf} = 32.174 \text{ ft-pdl}$$

Relationship between units of power—ft-pdl/sec and ft-lbf/sec. It is easy to see from the above that:

$$1 \frac{\text{ft-pdl}}{\text{sec}} = 0.031 \frac{\text{ft-lbf}}{\text{sec}}$$

$$1 \frac{\text{ft-lbf}}{\text{sec}} = 32.174 \frac{\text{ft-pdl}}{\text{sec}}$$

Since 1 horsepower (h.p.) = 550 (ft · lbf)/sec, we obtain:

$$1 \text{ h.p.} = 550 \cdot (32.174 \frac{\text{ft-pdl}}{\text{sec}}) = 1.77 \cdot 10^4 \frac{\text{ft-pdl}}{\text{sec}}$$

The relationships between other units in the f lbm s and f lbf s systems can be obtained in a similar manner.

7. OTHER UNITS OF MECHANICAL QUANTITIES

In addition to the units making up the MKS, cgs, MKGFS, f lbm s, and f lbf s systems, a number of units which do not belong to any system are also used.

We shall give the name *nonsystem units* to those units of measurement of physical quantities which are not part of a system of units, or which are obsolete.

Below we give the most common nonsystem units and their relationships with the MKS, cgs, and MKGFS systems. (The relationships of these units to units in the British system can be obtained using the methods of Section 4.)

Units of Length

The micron (μ) is one millionth of a meter:

$$1 \mu = 10^{-6} \text{ m} = 10^{-4} \text{ cm}$$

The millimicron (mμ) is one thousandth of a micron:

$$1 \text{ m}\mu = 10^{-9} \text{ m} = 10^{-7} \text{ cm}$$

The angstrom (Å) is one tenth of a millimicron:

$$1 \text{ Å} = 10^{-10} \text{ m} = 10^{-8} \text{ cm}$$

Units of Volume

The liter (l) is the volume of 1 kg of water at its greatest density (4° C) at normal atmospheric pressure:

$$1 \text{ l} = 10^{-3} \text{ m}^3 = 10^3 \text{ cm}^3$$

(the exact value of the liter is $1.000028 \cdot 10^{-3} \text{ m}^3$).

Units of Angular Velocity

The revolution per second (rps) is the angular velocity at which a rotating body completes 1 revolution in 1 second:

$$1 \text{ rps } = 2 \pi \frac{rad}{sec} = 6.28 \frac{rad}{sec}$$

The revolution per minute (rpm) is the angular velocity at which a rotating body completes 1 revolution in 1 minute:

$$1 \text{ rpm } = 0.105 \frac{rad}{sec}$$

Units of Mass

The metric ton is the unit of mass in the now obsolete MTS (meter, metric ton, second) system:

$$1 \text{ metric ton } = 10^3 \text{ kg } = 10^6 \text{ g } = 102 \text{ metric slugs}$$

The atomic mass unit (amu) is 1/16 of the mass of an atom of the lightest oxygen isotope $_8O^{16}$. The atomic mass unit is widely employed in atomic and nuclear physics.

$$1 \text{ amu } = 1.66 \cdot 10^{-27} \text{ kg } = 1.66 \cdot 10^{-24} \text{ g } = 1.70 \cdot 10^{-25} \text{ metric slugs}$$

The chemical mass unit (cmu) is 1/16 of the mean mass of atoms of natural oxygen, which is a mixture of the three isotopes $_8O^{16}$, $_8O^{17}$, $_8O^{18}$, making up natural oxygen in the proportion $506 : 0.204 : 1$. This means that the mean mass of natural oxygen atoms measured in atomic units of mass can be expressed as follows:

$$\frac{506 \cdot 16 + 0.204 \cdot 17 + 1 \cdot 18}{506 + 0.204 + 1} = 16.0044 \text{ amu}$$

which is equal to 16 cmu. The atomic weights of the chemical elements shown in the periodic table correspond to the numerical value of atomic masses measured in cmu.

The amu and the cmu are related in the following way:

$$1 \text{ amu } = 0.99972 \text{ cmu}$$
$$1 \text{ cmu } = 1.00028 \text{ amu}$$

For the mole see Chapter IV, Section 2.

Units of Force

The metric ton-force (T) is a unit of force equal to 1000 kgf:

$$1 \text{ T} = 9.81 \cdot 10^3 \text{ N} = 9.81 \cdot 10^8 \text{ dynes} = 10^3 \text{ kgf}$$

The short ton (sh. ton) and the long ton (l. ton) are units of force in the f lbf s system.

$$1 \text{ sh. ton} = 2000 \text{ lbf} = 8.90 \cdot 10^8 \text{ dynes}$$
$$1 \text{ l. ton} = 2240 \text{ lbf} = 9.96 \cdot 10^8 \text{ dynes}$$

The sten is the force which imparts a velocity of 1 m/sec to a mass of 1 metric ton. The sten is the unit of force in the MTS (meter-ton-second) system.

$$1 \text{ sten} = 10^3 \text{ N} = 10^8 \text{ dynes} = 102 \text{ kgf}$$

Units of Pressure

The standard (physical) atmosphere (atm) is the pressure exerted by a column of mercury (density 13.595 g/cm^3) 76 cm high subject to the normal acceleration due to gravity of 980.665 cm/sec^2.

$$1 \text{ atm} = 1.01 \cdot 10^5 \frac{\text{N}}{\text{m}^2} = 1.01 \cdot 10^6 \text{ baryes} = 1.01 \text{ bars} \cdot 10^4 \frac{\text{kgf}}{\text{m}^2}$$

The relationship between the standard (physical) atmosphere and the barye can be established in the following way. It is known that the pressure exerted by a column of liquid is determined by the equation:

$$p = d \cdot h = \rho g h$$

where d is the specific weight of the liquid, h is the height of the column of liquid, ρ is the density of the liquid, and g is the acceleration due to gravity.

Substituting numerical values into this equation, we find that a column of mercury 76 cm high exerts a pressure $p = 13.595$ g/cm^3 × 980.665 cm/sec$^2 \cdot$ 76 cm = $1.01 \cdot 10^6$ baryes.

The technical atmosphere is the pressure exerted by a force of 1 kgf on 1 cm^2:

$$1 \frac{\text{kgf}}{\text{cm}^2} = 9.81 \cdot 10^4 \frac{\text{N}}{\text{m}^2} = 9.81 \cdot 10^5 \text{ bars} = 10^4 \frac{\text{kgf}}{\text{m}^2}$$

A millimeter of mercury (m Hg or torr) is the pressure exerted by a mercury column 1 mm high (mercury density 13.595 g/cm^3) at the normal acceleration due to gravity of 980.665 cm/sec:

$$1 \text{ mm Hg} = 133 \frac{\text{N}}{\text{m}^2} = 1.33 \cdot 10^3 \text{ bars} = 13.6 \frac{\text{kgf}}{\text{m}^2} = 2.78 \frac{\text{lbf}}{\text{ft}^2}$$

A millimeter of water (mm H₂O) is the pressure exerted by a column of water (density 1 g/cm³) 1 mm high at the normal acceleration due to gravity of 980.665 cm/sec².

$$1 \text{ mm H}_2\text{O} = 9.81 \frac{N}{m^2} = 98.1 \text{ baryes} = 1 \frac{kgf}{m^2}$$

An inch of water at 4°C is the pressure exerted by a column of water 1 in high at 4°C and the normal acceleration due to gravity:

$$1 \text{ in H}_2\text{O} = 5.20 \frac{lbf}{ft^2}$$

The standard atmosphere in meteorology is the unit of pressure defined as follows:

$$1 \text{ bar} = 10^5 \text{ N/m}^2 = 10^6 \text{ baryes} = 1.02 \cdot 10^4 \text{ kgf/m}^2$$

A millibar (mbar) is one thousandth of a bar:

$$1 \text{ mbar} = 100 \text{ N/m}^2 = 10^3 \text{ baryes} = 10.2 \text{ kgf/m}^2$$

The pieza (pz) is the pressure exerted by a force of 1 sten on an area of 1 m². The pieza is the unit of pressure in the MTS system.

$$1 \text{ pz} = 10^3 \frac{N}{m^2} = 10^4 \text{ baryes} = 102 \frac{kgf}{m^2}$$

Units of Energy and Work

The kilojoule (kJ) is the work done by a force of 1 sten over a length of 1 meter. The kilojoule is the unit of work in the MTS system.

$$1 \text{ kilojoule} = 10^3 \text{ joules} = 10^{10} \text{ ergs} = 102 \text{ kgfm}$$

The watt-hour (wh) is the work done by 1 watt in 1 hour:

$$1 \text{ watt-hour} = 3600 \text{ joules} = 3.60 \cdot 10^{10} \text{ ergs} = 366 \text{ kgfm}$$

The kilowatt-hour (kwh) is the work done by 1 kilowatt in the course of 1 hour:

$$1 \text{ kilowatt-hour} = 3.60 \cdot 10^6 \text{ joules} = 3.60 \cdot 10^{13} \text{ ergs} =$$
$$3.66 \cdot 10^5 \text{ kgfm} = 1.34 \text{ horsepower-hours}$$

The watt-hour and kilowatt-hour are used chiefly for measuring the work done by electricity.

The electron-volt (ev) is the energy acquired by a particle with a charge equal to the elementary charge (electron charge) after passage through a potential difference of 1 volt:

$$1 \text{ ev} = 1.60 \cdot 10^{-19} \text{ J} = 1.60 \cdot 10^{-12} \text{ erg} = 1.63 \cdot 10^{-20} \text{ kgfm}$$

The relationship between the electron-volt and the erg can be established as follows. As is well known, the work done by an electric field in displacing a charge is expressed by the equation:

$$A = q \cdot U$$

where q is the magnitude of the charge and U is the potential difference.

Substituting into this equation the electron charge $e = 4.80 \cdot 10^{-10}$ cgce (q) and the voltage $U = 1 \text{ v} = 1/300$ cgs emu (U), we get:

$$1 \text{ ev} = 4.80 \cdot 10^{-10} \cdot \frac{1}{300} = 1.60 \cdot 10^{-12} \text{ erg}$$

The megaelectron-volt (Mev) is the unit of energy equal to one million electron-volts.

$$1 \text{ Mev} = 1.60 \cdot 10^{-13} \text{ joules} = 1.60 \cdot 10^{-6} \text{ erg} = 1.63 \cdot 10^{-14} \text{ kgfm}$$

The energy units ev and Mev are widely used in atomic and nuclear physics.

Units of Power

The kilowatt (kw) is the output at which 1 kilojoule of work is done in 1 sec:

$$1 \text{ kw} = 10^3 \text{ w} = 10^{10} \frac{\text{erg}}{\text{sec}} = 102 \frac{\text{kgfm}}{\text{sec}}$$

A metric horsepower is equal to 75 kgfm/sec:

$$1 \text{ metric h.p.} = 736 \text{ watts} = 7.36 \cdot 10^9 \frac{\text{erg}}{\text{sec}} = 75 \frac{\text{kgfm}}{\text{sec}} = 0.986 \text{ h.p.}$$

8. RULES FOR CALCULATION IN SOLVING PHYSICAL PROBLEMS

Errors often occur in the solving of physics problems because of incorrect usage of the units of measurement. In order to avoid such errors, the following rules should be observed.

1. Having obtained a theoretical formula for the solution of the problem, choose the most convenient system of units for calculating the unknown value. *

2. Express all quantities in the theoretical formula in units of the given system.

3. Substitute the numerical values of all quantities into the theoretical formula and perform the indicated calculations.

4. When writing the result of the calculation, also record the names of the units of measurement of the unknown quantity in the system in which the solution was derived.

5. Calculate the dimensions of the unknown by means of the theoretical formula. In order to do this, we must:

a) substitute into the theoretical formula the names of all the quantities appearing in it;

b) make all possible abbreviations;

c) replace the names of the units left after abbreviation by their dimensions, and make all possible abbreviations once more;

d) carry out the indicated operations with the names of the remaining fundamental units.

The result gives the dimensions of the unknown quantity.

6. Compare the dimensions derived** with the dimensions of the unit of measurement of the unknown quantity. If the dimensions are not identical, the solution is wrong.

Let us consider a few examples.

Example 1. Express the unit of force in the MKS system (N) in cgs units.

$$1 \text{ N} = 1 \times \frac{\text{kg} \cdot \text{m}}{\text{sec}^2} = 1 \times \frac{1000 \text{ g} \cdot 100 \text{ cm}}{\text{sec}^2} = 10^5 \cdot \frac{\text{g} \cdot \text{cm}}{\text{sec}^2} \text{ (dynes)}$$

$$1 \text{ N}^5 = 10 \text{ dynes}$$

Example 2. Express 1 erg in joules.

$$1 \text{ erg} = 1 \frac{\text{g} \cdot \text{cm}}{\text{sec}^2} = 1 \frac{0.001 \text{ kg} \cdot (0.01 \text{ m})^2}{\text{sec}^2} = 10^{-7} \frac{\text{kg} \cdot \text{m}^2}{\text{sec}^2} \text{ (J)}$$

$$1 \text{ erg} = 10^{-7} \text{ J}$$

Example 3. Express 1 kgfm/sec in units of power of the MKS system.

---

* Note. If both the denominator and numerator in the theoretical formula contain quantities of the same kind, raised to the same power, they need not be expressed in units of the system adopted for the problem, but can be expressed in units of any system, since the ratio of similar quantities raised to the same power is a dimensionless quantity. This ratio will remain the same regardless of the system of units.

** Note to points 5 and 6. The dimensions of the unknown quantity need not be calculated if there is absolute certainty that the solution is correct.

$$1 \ \frac{kgfm}{sec} = 1 \times \frac{9.81 \ N \cdot m}{sec} = 9.81 \ \frac{J}{sec} \text{ (watt)}$$

$$1 \ \frac{kgfm}{sec} = 9.81 \text{ watts}$$

Example 4. Express the unit of density of the cgs system (g/cm³) in the MKGFS system.

$$1 \ \frac{g}{cm^3} = 1 \times \frac{1.02 \cdot 10^{-4} \text{ metric slugs}}{(10^{-2} \ m)^3} = 102 \ \frac{\text{metric slugs}}{m^3} =$$

$$102 \ \frac{kgf \cdot sec^2}{m \cdot m^3} = 102 \ \frac{kgf \cdot sec^2}{m^4}$$

$$1 \ \frac{g}{cm^3} = 102 \ \frac{kgf \cdot sec^2}{m^4}$$

Example 5. Express a pressure of 1 technical atmosphere in MKS, cgs, and MKGFS units.
In the MKS system:

$$1 \text{ atm} = 1 \ \frac{kgf}{cm^2} = 1 \ \frac{9.81 \ N}{(0.01 \ m)^2} = 9.81 \cdot 10^4 \frac{N}{m^2}$$

$$1 \text{ atm} = 9.81 \cdot 10^4 \ \frac{N}{m^2}$$

In the cgs system:

$$1 \text{ atm} = 1 \frac{kgf}{cm^2} = 1 \ \frac{981,000 \text{ dynes}}{cm^2} = 9.81 \cdot 10^5 \ \frac{\text{dynes}}{cm^2} \text{ (bars)}$$

$$1 \text{ atm} = 9.81 \cdot 10^5 \text{ bars}$$

In the MKGFS system:

$$1 \text{ atm} = 1 \ \frac{kgf}{cm^2} = 1 \ \frac{kgf}{(0.01 \ m)^2} = 10^4 \ \frac{kgf}{m^2}$$

$$1 \text{ atm} = 10^4 \ \frac{kgf}{m^2}$$

Example 6. Express 1 kwh in units of work of the MKS, cgs, and MKGFS system.
In the MKS system:

$$1 \text{ kwh} = 1 \cdot 1000 \text{ wh} = 1 \cdot 1000 \cdot 3600 \text{ w} \cdot \text{sec (J)} = 3.6 \cdot 10^6 \text{ J}$$
$$1 \text{ kwh} = 3.6 \cdot 10^6 \text{ J}$$

In the cgs system:

$$1 \text{ kwh} = 3.6 \cdot 10^6 \text{ J} = 3.6 \cdot 10^6 \frac{\text{kg} \cdot \text{m}^2}{\text{sec}^2}$$

$$= 3.6 \cdot 10^6 \frac{(1000 \text{ g})(100 \text{ cm})^2}{\text{sec}^2} = 10^{13} \frac{\text{g} \cdot \text{cm}^2}{\text{sec}^2} \text{ (ergs)}$$

$$1 \text{ kwh} = 3.6 \cdot 10^{13} \text{ ergs}$$

In the MKGFS system:

$$1 \text{ kwh} = 3.6 \cdot 10^6 \text{ J} = 3.6 \cdot 10^6 \frac{\text{kg} \cdot \text{m}^2}{\text{sec}^2}$$

$$3.6 \cdot 10^6 \frac{\frac{1}{9.81} \text{ metric slugs} \cdot \text{m}^2}{\text{sec}^2} = \frac{3.6}{9.81} \times 10^6 \frac{\text{kgf} \cdot \text{sec}^2 \cdot \text{m}^2}{\text{m} \cdot \text{sec}^2}$$

$$= 3.7 \cdot 10^5 \text{ kgfm}$$

$$1 \text{ kwh} = 3.7 \cdot 10^5 \text{ kgfm}$$

Example 7. The weight of a body is 3 kgf. Find its mass.
Solution. The weight of a body and its mass are related as follows:

$$w = m \cdot g$$

This gives us the theoretical formula for calculating the mass:

$$m = \frac{w}{g}$$

Let us make the calculation in the MKS, cgs, and MKGFS systems.
Calculation in the MKS system
Let us express the quantities contained in the theoretical formula in units of this system:

$$w = 3 \text{ kgf} = 3 \cdot 9.81 \text{ N}$$
$$g = 9.81 \frac{\text{m}}{\text{sec}^2}$$

Substituting the numerical values of w and g, making the calculation, and remembering that in the MKS system mass is expressed in kg, we find:

$$m = \frac{w}{g} = \frac{3 \cdot 9.81}{9.81} = 3 \text{ kg}$$

Calculating the dimensions from the theoretical formula gives us the same result:

$$[m] = \frac{[w]}{[g]} = \frac{N}{\dfrac{m}{\sec^2}} = \frac{m \cdot kg \cdot \sec^{-2}}{m \cdot \sec^{-2}} = kg$$

Calculation in cgs system

In order to express quantities in the cgs system, we should re-member that 1 kgf = 981,000 dynes, and that acceleration due to gravity in this system is $g = 981$ cm/$\sec^2$. Consequently:

$$w = 3 \; Kgf = 3 \cdot 981,000 \; dynes$$
$$g = 981 \; \frac{cm}{\sec^2}$$

Substituting w and g into the theoretical formula, making the cal-culation, and remembering that in the cgs system mass is measured in grams, we find:

$$m = \frac{w}{g} = \frac{3 \cdot 981,000}{981} = 3000 \; grams$$

Let us calculate the dimensions from the theoretical formula:

$$[m] = \frac{[w]}{[g]} = \frac{dynes}{\dfrac{cm}{\sec^2}} = \frac{cm \cdot g \cdot \sec^{-2}}{cm \cdot \sec^{-2}} = grams$$

The dimensions coincide with those shown for mass in Table 2.

Calculation in the MKGFS system

$w = 3$ kgf
$g = 9.81$ m/$\sec^2$
Substituting the numerical values into the formula, we get:

$$m = \frac{3}{9.81} = 0.306 \; metric \; slug$$

Since the calculation is made for the MKGFS system, we add the name of the unit of mass in this system (metric slug) to the numeri-cal value.

The following incorrect answer to this example is often encoun-tered.

The data are written out as:
$w = 3$ kgf
$g = 9.81$ m/$\sec^2$
The numerical values are then substituted into the formula, the calculation is made and, without analyzing in which system the solution is found, or in which units the answer should be expressed, the answer is often given as:

$$m = \frac{w}{g} = \frac{3}{9.81} = 0.3 \; kg$$

This error is the result of ignoring the rules.

Chapter III

UNITS OF MEASUREMENT OF
ACOUSTIC QUANTITIES

We distinguish two types of quantities which describe sound.

Sound as a physical phenomenon, that is to say, as an oscillation (in the particles of an elastic medium) propagated in wave form, is described by frequency, sound pressure, sound energy density, sound energy flux, sound intensity, etc.

As a psycho-physical phenomenon (that is, as a specific sensation produced by the action of sound waves on the organ of hearing), sound is described primarily by two quantities: loudness and pitch.

There is a relationship between the quantities describing sound as a psycho-physical phenomenon and those describing it as a physical phenomenon. For example, pitch is associated with frequency. Loudness is a complex function of sound intensity and frequency.

Quantities describing sound as a physical phenomenon are measured in MKS, cgs, and MKGFS units. The intensity of sound, or more accurately, the sound intensity level, is also measured in nonsystem logarithmic units, that is, in bels, decibels, and nepers. The introduction of these logarithmic units is a result of the fact that the intensity of a sound determines its loudness, and the loudness is dependent on the logarithm of the intensity.

The units of measurement of quantities characterizing sound as a psycho-physical phenomenon are determined without relation to a system of units.

Below we consider the units of measurement used in acoustics.

1. UNITS OF MEASUREMENT OF QUANTITIES
CHARACTERIZING SOUND AS A PHYSICAL PHENOMENON

Frequency. The frequency of a sound is measured in cycles. The cycle (cps) is one oscillation per second. There is also a larger unit of frequency—the kilocycle. One kilocycle (kc) equals 10^3 cycles.

Sound pressure. When a sound wave strikes a surface, it exerts a pressure on it. The pressure caused by the sound varies periodically. At any given point in the medium, the pressure changes from maximum to zero and then returns to maximum (during one period of vibration). The maximum sound pressure (amplitude) is determined from the equation:

$$p_0 = \omega v \rho A \tag{3.1}$$

where ω is the angular frequency, v is the speed of sound, ρ is the density of the medium, and A is the amplitude of vibration of the particles.

The mean pressure over a period is determined from the equation:

$$\bar{p} = \frac{1}{2} \omega v \rho A \tag{3.2}$$

The units of pressure in the MKS, cgs, and MKGFS systems were determined earlier (see Chapter II, Section 1). The reader may wish to verify the fact that the right-hand side of Eq. (3.1) has the dimensions of pressure.

Sound energy density. The particles of the elastic medium through which sound waves are propagated undergo oscillatory motion and, therefore, possess kinetic and potential energy. This energy is termed *sound energy.*

The amount of sound energy contained in a unit volume of elastic medium is termed the *sound energy density.*

The density is determined from the equation:

$$w = k \cdot \frac{W}{V} \tag{3.3}$$

where W is the energy contained in the volume V.

Assuming, in Eq. (3.3), that $k = 1$, $W = 1$ joule, and $V = 1 \text{ m}^3$, we obtain the unit of measurement of sound energy density in the MKS system:

$$1 \text{ MKS } (w) = 1 \cdot \frac{1 \text{ J}}{1 \text{ m}^3} = 1 \frac{\text{J}}{\text{m}^3}$$

The unit of sound energy density in the MKS system is the energy density at which 1 joule of energy is concentrated in 1 m^3 of medium.

The dimensions of the sound energy density in the MKS system are:

$$[w] = \frac{[W]}{[V]} = \frac{\text{m}^2 \cdot \text{kg} \cdot \text{sec}^{-2}}{\text{m}^3} = \text{m}^{-1} \cdot \text{kg} \cdot \text{sec}^{-2}$$

Applying Eq. (3.3), we also find that the sound energy density is measured:

a) in the cgs system, in units of erg/cm³, which have the dimensions om⁻¹ · g · sec⁻²;

b) in the MKGFS system, in units of kgfm/m³, which have the dimensions m⁻² · kgf.

Sound energy flux. The sound energy flux through a surface is the amount of energy passing through the surface during one period (in a direction normal to the surface).

The sound energy flux Φ is determined from the equation:

$$\Phi = k\bar{w}TSv \qquad (3.4)$$

where $\bar{w}$ is the mean energy density for one period, S is the area of the surface, T is the period, and v is the speed of sound.

Setting $k = 1$, $\bar{w} = 1$ J/m³, $T = 1$ sec, $S = 1$ m², and $v = 1$ m/sec, we find that the unit of energy flux in the MKS system is:

$$1 \text{ MKS } (\Phi) = 1 \cdot 1\,\frac{J}{m^3} \cdot 1 \text{ sec} \cdot 1 \text{ m}^2 \cdot 1\,\frac{m}{\text{sec}} = 1 \text{ J}$$

From Eq. (3.4), we can also see that the sound energy flux is measured in ergs in the cgs system and in kgfm in the MKGFS system.

Mean sound energy flux. The mean sound energy flux through a surface is the average amount of energy per period passing through a given surface per unit of time. The mean flux $\bar{\Phi}$ is determined from the equation:

$$\bar{\Phi} = k\,\frac{\Phi}{T} = k\,\frac{\bar{w}TSv}{T} = k\bar{w}Sv \qquad (3.5)$$

Assuming, in Eq. (3.5), that $k = 1$, $\bar{w} = 1$ J/m³, $S = 1$ m², and $v = 1$ m/sec, we find that the unit of measurement for the mean flux in the MKS system is:

$$1 \text{ MKS } (\bar{\Phi}) = 1\,\frac{J}{\text{sec}} \text{ (watt)}$$

The unit of mean sound energy flux through a surface, in the MKS system, is the mean sound energy flux of the sound waves for which one joule of energy passes the given surface in one second.

The dimensions of this unit are:

$$[\bar{\Phi}] = [\bar{w}][S][v] = m^{-1} \cdot kg \cdot sec^{-2} \cdot m^2 \cdot m \cdot sec^{-1}$$
$$= m^2 \cdot kg \cdot sec^{-3}$$

We can also find, from Eq. (3.5), that the mean energy flux is measured:

a) in the cgs system, in erg/sec, with dimensions cm² · g · sec⁻³;

b) in the MKGFS system, in kgfm/sec, with dimensions m · kgf · sec⁻¹.

As can be seen from the above, the mean sound energy flux is measured in units of power (wattage).

Sound intensity (sound strength). The sound intensity (strength) I is the mean sound energy flux through a unit area:

$$I = k \frac{\bar{\Phi}}{S} \qquad (3.6)$$

where $\bar{\Phi}$ is the mean sound energy flux through the surface S.

Sound intensity can also be defined in the following way: the amount of sound energy, averaged per period, passing through a unit area per unit time.

Assuming, in Eq. (3.6), that $k = 1$, $\bar{\Phi} = 1$ J/sec, and $S = 1$ m², we find that the unit of sound intensity in the MKS system is:

$$1 \text{ MKS } (I) = 1 \frac{1 \dfrac{J}{\sec}}{1 \text{ m}^2} = 1 \frac{J}{\sec \cdot \text{m}^2} = 1 \frac{\text{watt}}{\text{m}^2}$$

The unit of sound intensity in the MKS system is taken as the intensity at which 1 joule of energy per period passes through 1 m² of a surface (perpendicular to the direction of propagation) in one second.

The dimensions of this unit are:

$$[I] = \frac{[\bar{\Phi}]}{[S]} = \frac{\text{m}^2 \cdot \text{kg} \cdot \sec^{-3}}{\text{m}^2} = \text{kg} \cdot \sec^{-3}$$

It also follows from Eq. (3.6) that sound intensity is measured:
a) in the cgs system, in erg/(sec · cm²), with dimensions g · sec⁻³;
b) in the MKGFS system, in kgfm/(sec · m²), with dimensions m⁻¹ · kgf · sec⁻¹.

These units of sound intensity (sound strength) are rarely used.

In practice we do not usually measure the absolute sound intensity but rather the intensity with respect to a zero intensity level. The zero intensity level is usually taken as a sound intensity of 10^{-16} watt/cm².

Let us denote the zero sound intensity level as I_0 and consider the ratio:

$$L = k \log_a \frac{I}{I_0} \qquad (3.7)$$

where I is the intensity of the measured sound.

The quantity L is termed the *sound intensity level* I with respect to the zero intensity level I_0, or simply the sound intensity level.

Using Eq. (3.7), we can derive two units of measurement for the level of sound intensity, depending on our choice of the logarithm base. If $a = 10$, that is, if we use common logarithms, Eq. (3.7) takes the form:

$$L = k \log \frac{I}{I_0} \qquad (3.8)$$

Assuming that $k = 1$ and $I = 10 \, I_0$, we get $L = 1$.

This abstract unit is called a bel and is taken as the unit of measurement of the sound intensity level.

The bel (b) is the intensity level of a sound for which the common logarithm of the ratio of the intensity of the sound to zero intensity is equal to unity.

The submultiple unit *decibel* is formed from the bel.

The decibel (db) is one tenth of a bel.

If we assume $a = e$ in Eq. (3.7), that is, if we use natural logarithms, we have:

$$L = k \log \frac{I}{I_0} \qquad (3.9)$$

Assuming that $k = 1$ and $I = e I_0$, we obtain $L = 1$.

This unit is called the neper and is taken as the unit of measurement of the sound intensity level.

The neper (nep) is the intensity level of a sound for which the natural logarithm of the ratio between the sound intensity and zero intensity is equal to unity.

The following relationships exist between the decibel and the neper:

$$
\begin{aligned}
1 \text{ b} &= 10 & \text{db} &= 2.30 \text{ nep} \\
1 \text{ db} &= 0.1 & \text{b} &= 0.230 \text{ nep} \\
1 \text{ nep} &= 0.434 \text{ b} & &= 4.34 \text{ db}
\end{aligned}
$$

2. UNITS OF MEASUREMENT OF QUANTITIES CHARACTERIZING SOUND AS A PSYCHO-PHYSICAL PHENOMENON

The problem of choosing units for measuring sound as a psycho-physical phenomenon is a difficult one. Hence, before considering these units, we should make some preliminary observations.

In considering sound as a psycho-physical phenomenon, we should point out that not every sound wave acting on the ear is capable of producing an auditory impression. For the sound to be audible, the frequency must lie roughly in the range 20 to 20,000 cps; vibrations with a frequency less than 20 or more than 20,000 cps cannot usually be heard by the ear; in addition, for the sound to produce an auditory impression, it must be of sufficient intensity.

The minimum sound intensity at which sound waves of a given frequency can be heard is called the *threshold of audibility*. A sound cannot be heard when its intensity falls below this threshold. The threshold is different for different frequencies.

Two sounds of different frequency, but with the same intensity, produce different auditory impressions. The ear reacts more sensitively to frequencies from 1000 to 3000 cycles. For these frequencies, the threshold of audibility is lowest. For the frequency 1000 cycles, the threshold is 10^{-9} er/sec $\cdot$ cm^2 (10^{-16} watt/cm^2). The ear is less sensitive to other frequencies, and the threshold of audibility for these frequencies is higher.

Loudness, which describes the perception of a sound, increases as the intensity of the sound is increased. However, there is no direct ratio between loudness and intensity. According to the Weber-Fechner law, as the intensity of a sound increases from I_0 to I, the loudness increases in proportion to the logarithm of the ratio $I : I_0$.

Using the Weber-Fechner law, we can construct a scale of units to measure loudness. This scale does not measure absolute loudness, but the loudness level of a sound compared to a given zero point (in the same way as was done for the intensity level).

If we express the loudness of a sound in terms of intensity, we obtain a complex logarithmic dependence. But if we express the level of loudness in terms of the level of intensity, we obtain a simple relationship. This is exactly why a logarithmic scale of units has been introduced for measuring the intensity of sound.

Loudness. The intensity of the auditory impression produced by a sound wave is termed the *loudness* of the sound. As was pointed out above, the loudness is a complex function of the intensity.

There are no units for measuring absolute loudness. Instead of measuring absolute loudness, we measure the loudness level of a sound as compared to a given zero. The zero is taken as the loudness of a standard sound (1000 cps) whose intensity is 10^{-16} watt/cm^2.

The unit of measurement of loudness level is the *phon*.

The phon is the loudness level of a standard sound with an intensity level of 1 decibel.

The phon is convenient for practical purposes, first, because one phon is the least perceptible variation in loudness level, and, second, because the loudness levels of the sounds usually encountered in everyday life can be expressed in phons by small numbers.

Below we give some examples of the loudness level of certain sound sources.

Source	Loudness level in phons
Passenger aircraft, 5 m from the side	120
Subway station when a train is passing	95
Street noise	60–85

Source	Loudness level in phons
Orchestra playing fortissimo	80–90
Office of typists	70–75
Loud conversation	70
Urban apartment	25–40
Noise at night in a city	30–40
Quiet whisper	10–15
Threshold of audibility	0

A loudness level of 130–140 phons hurts the ears and is termed the *threshold of feeling.*

In this case of the standard sound, the loudness level in phons is numerically equal to the intensity level in decibels. For example, a sound of standard frequency with an intensity level of 3 decibels has a loudness level of 3 phons.

The loudness level of sounds of other frequencies is a function of the frequency and the intensity level. In order to express the loudness level of a sound or noise, we have to compare it with the loudness level of a standard sound (1000 cps). The loudness level of any sound or noise expressed in phons is numerically equal to the intensity level of an equally loud standard sound expressed in decibels.

Pitch. Absolute pitch is measured in cycles per/second. *Relative* pitch is the relationship between two tones, or the ratio of two frequencies. This may also be expressed in terms of pitches on a musical scale.

Pitch is measured in savarts, octaves, and other units.

The savart is the interval for which the common logarithm of the ratio between the extreme frequencies (of the interval) is equal to 0.001. If ν_1 and ν_2 are the extreme frequencies of the pitch, the difference $\nu_2 - \nu_1$ is equal to 1 savart when:

$$\log \frac{\nu_2}{\nu_1} = 0.001 \tag{3.10}$$

The octave is the interval over which the ratio of the extreme frequencies is equal to 2. The interval $\nu_2 - \nu_1$ is equal to one octave if the following condition holds for the extreme frequencies:

$$\frac{\nu_2}{\nu_1} = 2 \tag{3.11}$$

The octave is used to form fractional units, the *millioctave* and the *cent.*

$$1 \text{ millioctave} = 10^{-3} \text{octave}$$
$$1 \text{ cent} = 1/1200 \text{ octave}$$

The following relationship exists between the octave and the savart:

$$1 \text{ octave} = 301 \text{ savarts}$$

since $\log 2 = 0.301.$ *

---

* Note: Although the metric system is used predominantly in acoustics, the British system may also be used. The units for acoustic quantities in the British system may be developed in a manner analogous to that employed above for the metric system. The reader may also obtain the units in the British system by using the results of this chapter and of Chapter II.

Chapter IV

UNITS OF MEASUREMENT OF QUANTITIES USED IN MOLECULAR PHYSICS

Until recently, there was no definite system of units for molecular physics. One reason for this was that one of the most important quantities in this branch of physics, heat, was measured in units which did not belong to any system of units. The unit of heat was the calorie, which is defined as the amount of heat required to heat 1 gram of pure water from 19.5 to 20.5°C at atmospheric pressure. In the British system, the unit of heat was the BTU (British Thermal Unit), which is defined as the amount of heat required to raise the temperature of 1 lbm of water one Fahrenheit degree.

If we logically develop the MKS and cgs systems of mechanical units for molecular physics, we ought to define the unit of heat by the equation:

$$Q = kW \qquad (4.1)$$

where Q is the heat, W is the work, and k is the proportionality factor. Assuming that $k = 1$, we find that the unit of heat in the MKS system is the joule or, more accurately, the heat equivalent to 1 joule of work. In the cgs system, it would be the heat equivalent to 1 erg of work, and in the British absolute system, the heat equivalent to one foot-poundal of work.

Historically speaking, however, the unit of heat, the calorie, was chosen before the law of equivalence of work and heat was discovered. Hence, Eq. (4.1) is not considered to be the fundamental equation for heat.

At the present time, systems of units based on the MKS and cgs mechanical quantities are being used more and more commonly in molecular physics.

The MKS system has the following fundamental quantities:

The meter(m)—the unit of length;
The kilogram(kg)—the unit of mass;
The second(sec)—the unit of time;
The degree(°)—the unit of temperature.

In physics, the cgs system* is often used to measure molecular and thermodynamic quantities and, in particular, heat quantities; the fundamental units of this system are:

The centimeter (cm)—the unit of length;

The gram (g)—the unit of mass;

The second (sec)—the unit of time;

The degree (°)—the unit of temperature.

Units based on the calorie are also used for measuring thermal quantities.

1. TEMPERATURE

Temperature is a fundamental quantity, and the unit of its measurement—the degree—is a fundamental unit in all systems of units in molecular physics.

The degree (°)** is a fraction of the difference between the basic reference points on a temperature scale.

The different temperatures of phase equilibrium have been selected as the reference points for different temperature scales. Here the differences between the reference points are divided into an equal number of fractions (degrees).

There are four common temperature scales: Celsius (C),*** Kelvin (K), Fahrenheit (F) and Réaumur (R). The temperature scales differ either in the point at which temperature readings begin, or in the magnitude of the degree, or in both.

Celsius Scale. On the Centigrade (Celsius) scale, the zero temperature is taken as the melting point of ice. A degree is taken as one hundredth of the difference between this point and the boiling point of water at atmospheric pressure at sea level. Thus, the melting point of ice on the Centigrade scale is 0°, and the boiling point of water is 100°.

Kelvin Scale (absolute). The zero reading on the Kelvin scale is taken as -273.16°C. This temperature is known as *absolute zero*. It has been demonstrated by thermodynamics that no temperature can exist below absolute zero. Hence there are no negative temperatures on the Kelvin scale.

The degree on the Kelvin scale is equal to the Centigrade degree.

Fahrenheit Scale. The zero reading on the Fahrenheit scale is the melting point of a mixture of snow and ammonium chloride. The degree

---

*We might expect the systems of units for thermal quantities to be termed MKSD and cgsd. The final letter "d" in these names stands for "degree." However, this name is not used, in order to simplify the terminology.

**The abbreviation "deg" is only used in dimension equations, for example $[c] = $ J/(kg · deg). The numerical values of temperature are followed by the abbreviations °C or °K, for example, 200°C or 400°K. Nowadays the ° is sometimes omitted.

***This scale, although formulated by Celsius, is commonly known as the centigrade (degree = 1/100 of the freezing to boiling range of water) scale.

is taken as one hundredth of the difference between this zero and the normal temperature of the human body. On the Fahrenheit scale the melting point of snow is +32°, and the boiling point of water is +212°.

Réaumur scale. The zero reading on this scale, as on the Centigrade scale, is taken as the melting point of ice. A degree is taken as one eightieth of the difference between this point and the boiling point of water. Thus, on the Réaumur scale, ice melts at 0°, and water boils at 80°.

On the basis of these points on the different scales, we can derive the following expression for converting one scale to another:

Table 6

Units of Measurement of

Name of quantity	Defining equation	Units of	
		MKS	
		Unit	Dimensions
Heat	$Q = W$	J	$m^2 \cdot kg \cdot sec^{-2}$
Calorific value	$q = \dfrac{Q}{m}$	$\dfrac{J}{kg}$	$m^2 \cdot sec^{-2}$
Coefficient of linear expansion	$\alpha = \dfrac{\Delta l}{l_0 \Delta t}$	—	deg^{-1}
Coefficient of volumetric expansion	$\beta = \dfrac{\Delta V}{V_0 \Delta t}$	—	deg^{-1}
Specific heat (heat capacity)	$c = \dfrac{Q}{m \Delta t}$	$\dfrac{J}{kg \cdot deg}$	$m^2 \cdot sec^{-2} \cdot deg^{-1}$
Molar heat (heat capacity)	$G = \mu c$	$\dfrac{J}{kmole \cdot deg}$	$m^2 \cdot kg \cdot sec^{-2} \cdot deg^{-1}$
Heat of fusion	$\lambda = \dfrac{Q}{m}$	$\dfrac{J}{kg}$	$m^2 \cdot sec^{-2}$
Heat of vaporization	$r = \dfrac{Q}{m}$	$\dfrac{J}{kg}$	$m^2 \cdot sec^{-2}$
Dynamic viscosity coefficient*	$\eta = \dfrac{F}{S} \dfrac{\Delta l}{\Delta v}$	—	$m^{-1} \cdot kg \cdot sec^{-1}$
Kinematic viscosity coefficient*	$v = \dfrac{\eta}{\rho}$	—	$m^2 \cdot sec^{-1}$
Surface tension coefficient*	$\sigma = \dfrac{F}{l}$	$\dfrac{N}{m}, \dfrac{J}{m^2}$	$kg \cdot sec^{-2}$
Thermal conductivity coefficient*	$\lambda = \dfrac{Ql}{S \tau \Delta t}$	—	$m \cdot kg \cdot sec^{-3} \cdot deg^{-1}$

* In accepted American terminology the word "coefficient" is frequently omitted.

$$\frac{t^\circ\,K - 273}{5} = \frac{t^\circ\,C}{5} = \frac{t^\circ\,R}{4} = \frac{t^\circ\,F - 32}{9} \qquad (4.2)$$

Let us illustrate the use of this formula. Let us assume that we are given a Centigrade temperature and are required to convert it into Fahrenheit degrees. To do this, we take the second and fourth terms from (4.2):

$$\frac{t^\circ\,C}{5} = \frac{t^\circ\,F - 32}{9}$$

This gives us a formula for the desired conversion:

Quantities in Molecular Physics

measurement		Other units		
cgs		Based on calories		Based on BTU (f lbm s and °F)
Unit	Dimensions	cgs	MKS	
erg	$cm^2 \cdot g \cdot sec^{-2}$	$\dfrac{cal}{(gram\text{-}calorie)}$	$\dfrac{kcal}{(kilogram\text{-}calorie)}$	BTU
$\dfrac{erg}{g}$	$cm^2 \cdot sec^{-2}$	$\dfrac{cal}{g}$	$\dfrac{kcal}{kg}$	$\dfrac{BTU}{lbm}$
deg^{-1}	deg^{-1}	—	—	—
deg^{-1}	deg^{-1}	—	—	—
$\dfrac{erg}{g \cdot deg}$	$cm^2 \cdot sec^{-2} \cdot deg^{-1}$	$\dfrac{cal}{g \cdot deg}$	$\dfrac{kcal}{kg \cdot deg}$	$\dfrac{BTU}{lbm \cdot deg}$
$\dfrac{erg}{mole \cdot deg}$	$cm^2 \cdot g \cdot sec^{-2} \cdot deg^{-1}$	$\dfrac{cal}{mole \cdot deg}$	$\dfrac{kcal}{kmole \cdot deg}$	—
$\dfrac{erg}{g}$	$cm^2 \cdot sec^{-2}$	$\dfrac{cal}{g}$	$\dfrac{kcal}{kg}$	$\dfrac{BTU}{lbm}$
$\dfrac{erg}{g}$	$cm^2 \cdot sec^{-2}$	$\dfrac{cal}{g}$	$\dfrac{kcal}{kg}$	$\dfrac{BTU}{lbm}$
poise	$cm^{-1} \cdot g \cdot sec^{-1}$	—	—	—
—	$cm^2 \cdot sec^{-1}$	—	—	—
$\dfrac{dyne}{cm}$	$g \cdot sec^{-2}$	—	—	—
—	$cm \cdot g \cdot sec^{-3} \cdot deg^{-1}$	$\dfrac{cal}{cm \cdot sec \cdot deg}$	$\dfrac{kcal}{m \cdot sec \cdot deg}$	$\dfrac{BTU \cdot in}{ft^2 \cdot sec \cdot deg}$

$$t^\circ F = \frac{9}{5} t^\circ C + 32 \tag{4.3}$$

We can similarly find formulas for converting temperatures from any scale to another.

The Centigrade and the Kelvin scales are used most frequently in physics; hence we should remember the following formulas for converting Centigrade to Kelvin, or Kelvin to Centigrade:

$$t^\circ K = t^\circ C + 273, \ \ t^\circ C = t^\circ K - 273 \tag{4.4}$$

or

$$T = t + 273, \ \ t = T - 273 \tag{4.5}$$

where T is the conventional symbol for Kelvin temperature and t is the symbol for Centigrade.

The degree is the fundamental unit of the system, and it is, therefore, a part of the dimensions of the derived units of measurement in molecular physics.

To obtain the derived units, we must expand the formulas for the laws governing molecular physics into a series satisfying the conditions given at the beginning of Chapter II. A series of this kind is shown in Table 6.

2. DERIVED MOLECULAR PHYSICS UNITS IN THE MKS AND CGS SYSTEMS.

Let us use the formulas in Table 6 to determine the derived units applicable to molecular physics.

Heat. Assuming, in Eq. (4.1), $k = 1$, $W = 1$ joule, we find that the unit of measurement of heat in the MKS system is the joule.

Similarly, we can determine the unit of heat in the cgs system, the erg; in the MKGFS system, the kgfm; and in the f lbm s system, the foot-poundal.

The dimensions of units for heat are the same as for energy units, that is:

$m^2 \cdot kg \cdot sec^{-2}$ in the MKS system,

$cm^2 \cdot g \cdot sec^{-2}$ in the cgs system,

$m \cdot kgf$ in the MKGFS system, and

$ft \cdot lbm \cdot sec$ in the f lbm s system.

Units of measurement of heat not included in any system are the following: gram-calorie (cal), the kilogram-calorie (kcal), and the British Thermal Unit (BTU).

When solving physical problems we use the following relationships between system units of heat and nonsystem units:

1 cal = 4.18 J = 4.18 · 10^7 erg = 0.427 kgfm = 99.3 ft-pdl = 3.97 · 10^{-3} BTU

1 kcal = 4.18 · 10^3 J = 4.18 · 10^{10} erg = 427 kgfm = 9.93 · 10^4 ft-pdl = 3.97 BTU

1 J = 0.239 cal = 2.39 · 10^{-4} kcal = 9.48 · 10^{-4} BTU

1 erg = 2.39 · 10^{-8} cal = 2.39 · 10^{-11} kcal = 9.48 · 10^{-11} BTU

1 kgfm = 2.34 cal = 2.34 · 10^{-3} kcal = 9.30 · 10^{-3} BTU

1 BTU = 2.50 · 10^4 ft-pdl = 107.56 kgfm = 1.05 · 10^{10} ergs = 1.05 · 10^3 J = 252.0 cal

1 ft-pdl = 4.00 · 10^{-5} BTU = 4.30 · 10^{-3} kgfm = 4.21 · 10^5 ergs = 1.01 · 10^{-2} cal

Calorific value of a fuel. The unit of measurement of the calorific value q is determined by:

$$q = k \frac{Q}{m} \tag{4.6}$$

where Q is the amount of heat generated in combustion of m units of mass of the fuel.

Assuming, in (4.6), that $k = 1$, $Q = 1$ J, and $m = 1$ kg, we find that the unit of measurement for the calorific value in the MKS system is:

$$1 \text{ MKS } (q) = 1 \cdot \frac{1 \text{ J}}{1 \text{ kg}} = 1 \frac{\text{J}}{\text{kg}}$$

The unit of calorific value in the MKS system is taken as the calorific value of 1 kg of fuel which releases 1 joule of heat upon total combustion.

The dimensions of this unit are found from Eq. (4.6):

$$[q] = \frac{[Q]}{[m]} = \frac{\text{m}^2 \cdot \text{kg} \cdot \text{sec}^{-2}}{\text{kg}} = \text{m}^2 \cdot \text{sec}^{-2}$$

Analogously, from Eq. (4.6), we find that the calorific value is measured as follows:

in the cgs system, in units of erg/g, with dimensions $\text{cm}^2 \cdot \text{sec}^{-2}$;

in the MKGFS system, in units of kgfm/metric slug, with dimensions $\text{m}^2 \cdot \text{sec}^{-2}$;

in the f lbm s system, in units of ft-pdl/lbm, with dimensions $\text{ft}^2 \cdot \text{sec}^{-2}$.

In practice, the calorific value is usually measured in units not belonging to any system (i.e., in nonsystem units): cal/g, kcal/g, or BTU/lbm.

Coefficient of linear expansion. The unit of measurement of the coefficient of linear expansion α is determined by the equation:

$$\alpha = k \frac{\Delta l}{l_0 \Delta t} \tag{4.7}$$

where l_0 is the length of the body at 0°C and Δl is the absolute elongation of the body when the temperature is increased by Δt.

It follows from Eq. (4.7) that the unit of measurement of the coefficient of linear expansion is the same in all systems of units. Assuming that $k = 1$, $\Delta l = l_0$, and $\Delta t = 1°$, we find that the unit of measurement of the coefficient of linear expansion is:

1 unit of coefficient of linear expansion =

$$1 \cdot \frac{l_0}{l_0 \cdot 1 \text{ deg}} = 1 \text{ deg}^{-1}$$

The unit of measurement of the coefficient of linear expansion is taken as the coefficient of linear expansion of a substance which doubles its length when heated from 0° to 1°C.

The dimensions of this unit are the same in all systems: $\deg^{-1}$. (Of course, °F ≠ °C).

Coefficient of volumetric expansion. The unit of the coefficient of volumetric expansion β is determined from the equation:

$$\beta = k \frac{\Delta V}{V_0 \Delta t} \tag{4.8}$$

where V_0 is the volume of the body at 0°C and ΔV is the absolute increase in volume of the body when the temperature is increased Δt.

Assuming, in Eq. (4.8), that $k = 1$, $\Delta V = V_0$, and $\Delta t = 1°$, we find that:

1 unit of coefficient of volumetric expansion =

$$1 \cdot \frac{V_0}{V_0 \cdot 1 \text{ deg}} = 1 \text{ deg}^{-1}$$

The unit of the coefficient of volumetric expansion is taken as the coefficient of volumetric expansion of a substance which doubles its volume when heated from 0° to 1°C.

The dimensions of the unit of measurement of the coefficient of volumetric expansion are the same in all systems of units: $\deg^{-1}$.

Specific heat (heat capacity). The unit of specific heat c is determined from the equation:

$$Q = k c m \Delta t$$

where Q is the amount of heat required to raise the temperature of a body with mass m by Δt deg. This formula gives:

$$c = \frac{1}{k} \frac{Q}{m \Delta t} \tag{4.9}$$

2. DERIVED UNITS IN MOLECULAR PHYSICS

Assuming that $k = 1$, $m = 1$ kg, $Q = 1$ J, and $\Delta t = 1°C$, we find that the unit of heat capacity in the MKS system is:

$$1 \text{ MKS } (c) = 1 \cdot \frac{1 \text{ J}}{1 \text{ kg} \cdot 1 \text{ deg}} = 1\frac{\text{J}}{\text{kg} \cdot \text{deg}}$$

The unit of specific heat (heat capacity) in the MKS system is the specific heat of a substance which requires 1 joule of heat to raise the temperature of 1 kg of that substance by 1°C.

It follows from Eq. (4.9) that the dimensions of this unit are:

$$[c] = \frac{[Q]}{[m][\Delta t]} = \frac{\text{m}^2 \cdot \text{kg} \cdot \text{sec}^{-2}}{\text{kg} \cdot \text{deg}} = \text{m}^2 \cdot \text{sec}^{-2} \cdot \text{deg}^{-1}$$

In a similar fashion, we find that the heat is measured as follows:

in the cgs system, in $\frac{\text{erg}}{\text{g} \cdot \text{deg}}$, with dimension $\text{cm}^2 \cdot \text{sec}^{-2} \cdot \text{deg}^{-1}$;

in the MKGFS system, in kgfm/(metric slug · deg), with dimensions $\text{m}^2 \cdot \text{sec}^{-2} \cdot \text{deg}^{-1}$;

in the f lbm s system, in ft-pdl/(lbm · deg), with dimensions $\text{ft}^2 \cdot \text{sec}^{-2} \cdot \text{deg}^{-1}$.

In practice, the specific heat is usually measured in nonsystem units: cal/(g · deg), kcal/(kg · deg), or BTU/(lbm · deg).*

In engineering practice, the volumetric heat capacity is frequently used instead of the specific heat.

The *volumetric heat capacity* is the amount of heat required to raise the temperature of a unit volume of a substance 7 C°.** In the case of gases, the volumetric heat capacity is computed per m³ of gas at normal temperature and pressure, that is, at 0°C and 760 mm Hg: 1 m³ of gas at normal temperature and pressure is denoted as 1 nm³.

The volumetric heat capacity is measured in kcal/(nm³ · deg).

Molar heat capacity. The unit of measurement of molar heat capacity C is determined by the equation:

$$C = k\mu c \tag{4.10}$$

where μ is the mass of one mole of substance.***

Assuming, in Eq. (4.10), that $k = 1$, $\mu = 1$ kg/kmole, and $c = 1$ J/(kg · deg), we find the unit of measurement of the molar heat capacity in the MKS system:

---

*Whenever degrees appear in an expression with BTU, they are understood to be degrees Fahrenheit. In an expression with cal or kcal, they are degrees centigrade.
**The symbol °C denotes a temperature; C° denotes a temperature difference.
***A mole of a substance is a mass numerically equal (in grams) to the molecular weight of the substance. The mole is an individual unit of mass; that is, it relates only to a given substance. If the molecular weight of a substance is M, then for the substance, 1 mole = M (grams), and the mass of one mole is $\mu = M$ g/mole. For example, $\mu = 2$ g/mole for hydrogen, $\mu = 32$ g/mole for oxygen, and so on. The kmole of a substance is the mass numerically equal (in kilograms) to the molecular weight.

$$1 \text{ MKS } (C) = 1 \cdot 1 \frac{\text{kg}}{\text{kmole}} \cdot 1 \frac{\text{J}}{\text{kg} \cdot \text{deg}} = 1 \frac{\text{J}}{\text{kmole} \cdot \text{deg}}$$

The unit of molar heat capacity in the MKS system is taken as the molar heat capacity of a substance for which 1 J is required to raise the temperature of 1 kmole by 1 C°.

The dimensions of the unit of molar heat capacity are found in the MKS system from Eq. (4.10):

$$[C] = [\mu][c] = \text{kg} \cdot \text{m}^2 \cdot \text{sec}^{-2} \cdot \text{deg}^{-1} = \text{m}^2 \cdot \text{kg} \cdot \text{sec}^{-2} \cdot \text{deg}^{-1}$$

We can similarly find that the molar heat capacity in the cgs system is measured in erg/(mole · deg), the dimensions of which are $\text{cm}^2 \cdot \text{g} \cdot \text{sec}^{-2} \cdot \text{deg}^{-1}$.

In practice, the molar heat capacity is usually measured in cal/(mole · deg) and kcal/(kmole · deg).

Heat of fusion. The unit of measurement for the heat of fusion λ is determined from the equation:

$$Q = k\lambda m$$

where Q is the amount of heat required to melt m units of mass of a substance at its melting point. This formula yields:

$$\lambda = \frac{1}{k} \frac{Q}{m} \qquad (4.11)$$

Assuming that $k = 1$, $Q = 1$ J, and $m = 1$ kg, we obtain the unit of measurement of the heat of fusion in the MKS system:

$$1 \text{ MKS } (\lambda) = 1 \cdot \frac{1 \text{ J}}{1 \text{ kg}} = 1 \frac{\text{J}}{\text{kg}}$$

As the unit of the heat of fusion, we take the heat of fusion of a substance for which 1 joule of heat is required to melt 1 kg at the melting point.

The dimensions of this unit are:

$$[\lambda] = \frac{[Q]}{[m]} = \frac{\text{m}^2 \cdot \text{kg} \cdot \text{sec}^{-2}}{\text{kg}} = \text{m}^2 \cdot \text{sec}^{-2}$$

Similarly, we find that the heat of fusion is measured as follows: in the cgs system, in erg/g, with dimensions $\text{cm}^2 \cdot \text{sec}^{-2}$;

in the MKGFS system, in kgfm/metric slug, with dimensions $\text{m}^2 \cdot \text{sec}^{-2}$;

in the f lbm s system, in ft-pdl/lbm, with dimensions $\text{ft}^2 \cdot \text{sec}^{-2}$.

In practice, however, the heat of fusion is usually measured in nonsystem units: cal/g, kcal/kg, or BTU/lbm.

Heat of vaporization. The unit of heat of vaporization r can be found from the equation:

$$Q = krm$$

where Q is the amount of heat required to convert m units of mass of a liquid at its boiling point into vapor. This formula gives:

$$r = \frac{1}{k}\frac{Q}{m} \qquad (4.12)$$

Assuming, in (4.12), that $k = 1$, $Q = 1$ J, and $m = 1$ kg, we find that the unit of the heat of vaporization in the MKS system is:

$$1 \text{ MKS } (r) = 1 \cdot \frac{1 \text{ J}}{1 \text{ kg}} = 1\frac{\text{J}}{\text{kg}}$$

The unit of heat of vaporization in the MKS system is taken as the heat of vaporization of a liquid for which 1 joule of heat is required to convert 1 kg (at the boiling point) into vapor.

The dimensions of this unit are:

$$[r] = \frac{[Q]}{[m]} = \frac{\text{m}^2 \cdot \text{kg} \cdot \text{sec}^{-2}}{\text{kg}} = \text{m}^2 \cdot \text{sec}^{-2}$$

Analogously, we find that the heat of vaporization is measured as follows:

in the cgs system, in erg/g, with dimensions $\text{cm}^2 \cdot \text{sec}^{-2}$;

in the MKGFS system, in kgfm/metric slug, with dimensions $\text{m}^2 \cdot \text{sec}^{-2}$;

in the f lbm s system, in ft-pdl/lbm, with dimensions $\text{ft}^2 \cdot \text{sec}^{-2}$.

In practice, however, the specific heat of vaporization is usually measured in cal/g, kcal/kg, or BTU/lbm.

Dynamic viscosity coefficient. The unit of measurement of the dynamic viscosity coefficient (or simply dynamic viscosity) is determined from the equation:

$$\eta = k\frac{F}{S} \cdot \frac{\Delta l}{\Delta v} \qquad (4.13)$$

where F is friction over the area S; Δv is the difference between the velocities of the layers of liquid or gas over the distance Δl.

Assuming, in (4.13), that $k = 1$, $S = 1$ m², $F = 1$ N, $\Delta v = 1$ m/sec, and $\Delta l = 1$ m, we find that the unit for the dynamic viscosity in the MKS system is:

$$1 \text{ MKS } (\eta) = 1 \cdot \frac{1 \text{ N}}{1 \text{ m}^2} \cdot \frac{1 \text{ m}}{1 \text{ m/sec}} = 1\frac{\text{N} \cdot \text{sec}}{\text{m}^2}$$

The unit of measurement for dynamic viscosity in the MKS system is taken as the dynamic viscosity of a liquid (or gas) in which a friction of 1 N exists over an area of 1 m² between two layers moving with a transverse velocity gradient of 1 (m/sec)/m with respect to each other.

The dimensions of this unit are determined from Eq. (4.13):

$$[\eta] = \frac{[F]}{[S]} \cdot \frac{[\Delta l]}{[\Delta v]} = \frac{m \cdot kg \cdot sec^{-2} \cdot m}{m^2 \cdot m \cdot sec^{-1}} = m^{-1} \cdot kg \cdot sec^{-1}$$

Equation (4.13) shows that dynamic viscosity in the cgs system is measured in (dyne · sec)/cm², with dimensions cm⁻¹· g · sec⁻¹. This unit is called a *poise*. The poise is the viscosity at which one dyne acts on 1 cm² of a liquid (or gas) layer moving with a transverse velocity gradient of 1 (cm/sec)/cm with respect to another layer.

In the MKGFS system, the dynamic viscosity is measured in (kgf · sec)/m², with dimensions m⁻²· kgf · sec.

Kinematic viscosity coefficient. The unit of measurement of the kinematic viscosity coefficient (or simply kinematic viscosity) ν is determined by:

$$\nu = k\frac{\eta}{\rho} \qquad (4.14)$$

where ρ is the density of the liquid (gas).

Assuming here that $k = 1$, $\rho = 1$ kg/m³, and $\overset{\bullet}{\eta} = 1$ (N · sec)/m², we find the unit of kinematic viscosity in the MKS system:

$$1 \text{ MKS } [\nu] = 1 \cdot \frac{1\dfrac{N \cdot sec}{m^2}}{1\dfrac{kg}{m^3}} = 1\frac{m^2}{sec}$$

The dimensions of this unit are:

$$[\nu] = \frac{[\eta]}{[\rho]} = \frac{m^{-1}\cdot kg \cdot sec^{-1}}{kg \cdot m^{-3}} = m^2 \cdot sec^{-1}$$

Similarly, we find that the coefficient of kinematic viscosity is measured as follows:

in the cgs system, in cm²/sec, with dimensions cm² · sec⁻¹. This unit is called the stoke (st);

in the MKGFS system, in m²/sec with dimensions m² · sec⁻¹.

Surface tension coefficient. The unit of the surface tension coefficient (or simply surface tension) σ is determined by:

$$\sigma = k\frac{F}{l} \qquad (4.15)$$

where F is the surface tension along a periphery of length l bounding the surface of a liquid.

Assuming, in (4.15), that $k = 1$, $F = 1$ N, and $l = 1$ m, we find that the unit of surface tension in the MKS system is:

$$1 \text{ MKS } (\sigma) = 1 \cdot \frac{1 \text{ N}}{1 \text{ m}} = 1 \frac{\text{N}}{\text{m}}$$

The unit of surface tension in the MKS system is taken as the unit of surface tension of a liquid in which 1 N of force acts on 1 m of surface periphery.

The dimensions of this unit are:

$$[\sigma] = \frac{[F]}{[l]} = \frac{\text{m} \cdot \text{kg} \cdot \text{sec}^{-2}}{\text{m}} = \text{kg} \cdot \text{sec}^{-2}$$

Equation (4.15) also shows us that the surface tension is expressed as follows:

in the cgs system, in dyne/cm, with dimensions $\text{g} \cdot \text{sec}^{-2}$;

in the MKGFS system, in kgf/m, with dimensions $\text{m}^{-1} \cdot \text{kgf}$.

The unit of measurement of surface tension can also be determined from the formula:

$$\sigma = k \frac{W}{S} \tag{4.16}$$

where W is the free energy of the surface layer of a liquid with an area S.

If we take (4.16) as the fundamental equation, instead of (4.15), 1 J/m^2 can be taken (in the MKS system) as the unit of measurement of surface tension, that is, the surface tension of a liquid 1 m^2 of whose surface possesses 1 joule of free energy.

Thermal conductivity. The unit of thermal conductivity can be determined from the equation:

$$\lambda = k \cdot \frac{Ql}{S\tau\Delta t} \tag{4.17}$$

where Q is the amount of heat transferred through an area S of a layer of thickness l in the time τ, and Δt is the temperature difference between the surfaces bounding this layer.

Assuming, in (4.17), that $k = 1$, $Q = 1$ J, $l = 1$ m, $S = 1$ m^2, $\tau = 1$ sec, and $\Delta t = 1°$, we find that:

$$1 \text{ MKS } (\lambda) = 1 \cdot \frac{1 \text{ J} \cdot 1 \text{ m}}{1 \text{ m}^2 \cdot 1 \text{ sec} \cdot 1 \text{ deg}} = 1 \frac{\text{J}}{\text{m} \cdot \text{sec} \cdot \text{deg}} = 1 \frac{\text{watt}}{\text{m} \cdot \text{deg}}$$

The unit of thermal conductivity in the MKS system is taken as the thermal conductivity of a substance in which 1 joule of heat is transferred through 1 m² of a layer 1 m thick in 1 second, when the temperature difference between the surfaces bounding this layer is 1°. The dimensions of this unit are:

$$[\lambda] = \frac{[Q][l]}{[S][\tau][\Delta t]} = \frac{m^2 \cdot kg \cdot sec^{-2} \cdot m}{m^2 \cdot sec \cdot deg} = m \cdot kg \cdot sec^{-3} \cdot deg^{-1}$$

Similarly, we find that the coefficient of thermal conductivity is measured as follows:

in the cgs system, in erg/(cm · sec · deg), with dimensions cm · g · sec⁻³· deg⁻¹;

in the MKGFS system, in kgf/(sec · deg), with dimensions kgf · sec⁻¹· deg⁻¹;

in the f lbm s system, in ft-pdl/(ft · sec · deg [F]), with dimensions ft · lbm · sec⁻³· deg⁻³.

In practice, thermal conductivity is usually measured in nonsystem units: $\dfrac{cal}{cm \cdot sec \cdot deg}$, $\dfrac{kcal}{m \cdot hour\ deg}$, and $\dfrac{BTU \cdot in}{ft^2 \cdot sec \cdot deg}$.

3. SOLUTION OF PROBLEMS IN
MOLECULAR PHYSICS

In solving problems in molecular physics, calculations should be based on the same rules as those considered in Chapter II.

It should be remembered that the numerical values of the quantities in molecular physics (calorific value, specific heat, heat of fusion, etc.) referred to in textbooks and reference books are usually given in nonsystem units, that is, in cal, kcal, or BTU. When substituting these values into the theoretical formulas, we should express these quantities in units of the system in which the calculation is being carried out (using the relations between energy units given at the beginning of Section 2 of this chapter).

Let us consider a problem in molecular physics.

What is the increase in temperature of water which has fallen from a height of 15 m, assuming the total energy of fall is converted into heat and used in heating the water?

Solution. According to the above:

$$W = Q \tag{1}$$

where W is the potential energy of the water and Q is the heat produced by that energy.

Equation (1) can be written in the form:

$$mgH = mc\Delta t \tag{2}$$

where m is the mass of the water, H is the height from which it falls, g is the acceleration due to gravity, c is the specific heat of water, and Δt is the increase in temperature. Equation (2) gives us:

$$\Delta t = \frac{gH}{c} \tag{3}$$

Let us make the calculation in the MKS, cgs, and f lbm s systems. In the MKS system, the calculation is as follows:

$$H = 15 \text{ m, } g = 9.81 \frac{\text{m}}{\text{sec}^2}$$

As is well known, the specific heat of water is:

$$c = 1 \frac{\text{kcal}}{\text{kg} \cdot \text{deg}}$$

Before substituting this value into Eq. (3), let us express the specific heat in MKS units. To do this, we express the kilocalories in terms of the unit of heat capacity in MKS units, the joule:

$$1 \text{ kcal} = 4.18 \cdot 10^3 \text{ J}$$

consequently:

$$c = 1 \frac{\text{kcal}}{\text{kg} \cdot \text{deg}} = \frac{4.18 \cdot 10^3 \text{ J}}{\text{kg} \cdot \text{deg}} = 4.18 \cdot 10^3 \frac{\text{J}}{\text{kg} \cdot \text{deg}}$$

Substituting H, g and c into the theoretical formula, we obtain:

$$\Delta t = \frac{9.81 \cdot 15}{4.18 \cdot 10^3} = 0.035 \text{C}^\circ$$

It is interesting to note the following dependence between the height of fall of water and the increase in its temperature (assuming the kinetic energy is converted entirely into heat). Solving the problem for water falling from 427 meters by the above method, we find that its temperature increases 1C°. This means that for each meter of fall the temperature increases by 1/427 of a degree. Thus, the dependence between the height of fall and the increase in temperature can be given as:

$$\Delta t = \frac{H}{427} \text{C}^\circ$$

where Δt is the increase in temperature in degrees and H is the numerical value of the height in meters.

The same calculation in the cgs system gives us:

$$g = 981 \frac{cm}{sec^2}, \; H = 15 \text{ m} = 1500 \text{ cm}$$

$$c = 1 \frac{cal}{g \cdot deg} = 4.18 \cdot 10^7 \frac{erg}{g \cdot deg}$$

Substituting the numerical values of the quantities into the formula for temperature difference, we obtain:

$$\Delta t = \frac{981 \cdot 1500}{4.18 \cdot 10^7} = 0.035 \text{C}°$$

In the f lbm s system, we have:

$$H = 15 \text{ m} = 15(3.28 \text{ ft}) = 49.2 \text{ ft}$$
$$g = 32.174 \frac{ft}{sec^2}$$
$$c = 1 \frac{BTU}{lbm \cdot deg} = 1 \cdot \frac{2.50 \cdot 10^4 \text{ ft-pdl}}{lbm \cdot deg}$$

Substituting the numerical values of the quantities into the formula, we obtain:

$$\Delta t = \frac{32.174 \cdot 49.2}{2.50 \cdot 10^1} = 0.0639 \text{F}°$$

The dimensions of the result can be checked by the theoretical formula:

$$[\Delta t] = \frac{[g][H]}{[c]} = \frac{\dfrac{ft}{sec^2} \cdot ft}{\dfrac{ft\text{-}pdl}{lbm \cdot deg}} = \frac{ft^2 \cdot lbm \cdot deg}{sec^2 \cdot ft\text{-}pdl} =$$

$$= \frac{ft^2 \cdot lbm \cdot deg \text{ (F)} \cdot sec^2}{sec^2 \cdot ft \cdot ft \cdot lbm} = deg \text{ (F)}$$

Noting that $1 \text{F}° = \frac{5}{9} \text{C}°$, we can check our result with the previous one:

$$0.063 \text{F}° = (0.063)\frac{5}{9}\text{C}° = 0.035 \text{ C}°$$

Chapter V

SYSTEMS OF UNITS FOR MEASUREMENT OF ELECTROMAGNETIC QUANTITIES

The domain of electric and magnetic phenomena is not an isolated one. Electromagnetic phenomena are closely related to mechanical phenomena, and electromagnetic equations contain many mechanical quantities such as length, mass, velocity, acceleration, force, and energy. These units of measurement have already been determined and it is, therefore, natural to base systems of units for electric and magnetic quantities on the systems of mechanical units.

However, the mechanical units cannot be automatically extended to cover electric and magnetic phenomena. In constructing the systems of units for mechanical quantities, we saw that to determine the unit of measurement of a given physical quantity we needed an equation which contained only one unknown unit of measurement. However, among the equations for electromagnetic quantities, we will not find a single one which contains only one electromagnetic quantity (in addition to the mechanical quantities). Every electromagnetic equation contains at least two electric or magnetic quantities. In order to use an equation containing two new quantities, we must consider one of these quantities to be fundamental. In other words, we select the unit of measurement of one quantity arbitrarily. We will follow this procedure in constructing systems of units for measuring electromagnetic quantities.

In the MKSA system, the fourth fundamental quantity is the *current*; in the cgs esu system, it is the *dielectric permittivity* of a medium; and in the cgs emu system, it is the *magnetic permeability* of a medium.

In the following sections we will consider these systems and, in addition, the rationalized MKSA system as well as the cgs (Gaussian) system, which is a combination of the cgs esu and cgs emu systems.

1. THE MKSA (PRACTICAL) SYSTEM

The MKSA system is derived by expanding the MKS system to the domain of electric and magnetic quantities by the addition of one more fundamental unit.

The fundamental units in the system are:
The meter (m)—the unit of length;
The kilogram (kg)—the unit of mass;
The second (sec)—the unit of time;
The ampere (amp)—the unit of current.

"The ampere (amp) is the strength of an unvarying current, sustained in two parallel rectilinear conductors of infinite length and negligibly small cross section separated by a distance of 1 meter in a vacuum, producing a force between these conductors equal to $2 \cdot 10^{-7}$ newtons per meter of length" (adopted by the IX General Conference on Weights and Measures).

The ampere was selected arbitrarily as a fundamental unit of the system. However, its choice was influenced by the fact that it is of convenient size for practical applications, and that it is directly related to the unit of current in the cgs emu system. The ampere is equal to one tenth of an abampere,* which is the unit of current in the cgs emu system (cf. Section 3).

In order to construct the MKSA system, we must define the derived units by using a series of electromagnetic equations satisfying the conditions presented in Chapter I, Section 2. Such a series is shown in Table 7. Using the fundamental equations given in this table, we can determine the units of measurement of electromagnetic quantities in the MKSA system.

Charge. The unit of charge is determined from the equation:

$$q = kIt \tag{5.1}$$

where q is the charge transferred across a cross section of a conductor in time t when the current is I.

Assuming, in this equation, that $k = 1$, $I = 1$ amp, and $t = 1$ sec, we find:

$$1 \text{ unit of charge } = 1 \text{ amp} \cdot 1 \text{ sec} = 1 \text{ amp} \cdot \text{sec}$$

The unit of charge in the MKSA system is called the *coulomb*. The coulomb is the charge carried in a conductor by a current of 1 amp in 1 sec.

It follows from Eq. (5.1) that the dimensions of the coulomb are:

$$[q] = [I][t] = \text{amp} \cdot \text{sec} = \text{sec} \cdot \text{amp}$$

---

*The absolute ampere is different from the international ampere, which was used earlier.

The *international ampere* is defined as "the unvarying current which deposits 0.001118 g of silver from an aqueous solution of silver nitrate in 1 sec." The absolute and international amperes are related in the following way:
1 absolute ampere = 1.000165 ± 0.000025 int. ampere
1 int. ampere = 0.99985 absolute ampere.

Surface charge density. The unit of surface charge density is determined by the equation:

$$\sigma = k\frac{q}{S} \tag{5.2}$$

Assuming, in this equation, that $k = 1$, $q = 1$ coulomb, and $S = 1$ m^2, we obtain:

$$1 \text{ unit of surface charge density } = 1 \cdot \frac{1 \text{ coulomb}}{1 \text{ m}^2} = 1\frac{\text{coulomb}}{\text{m}^2}.$$

The unit of surface charge density in the MKSA system is taken as the charge density created by a charge of 1 coulomb uniformly distributed over a surface area of 1 m^2. This unit has no particular name.

Let us agree, as was done in the section on mechanical units, to denote the units of measurement without special names by the abbreviation for the system of units followed by the symbol for the measured quantity in parentheses. Thus, the unit of surface charge density is designated as MKSA (σ).

The dimensions of the unit of surface charge density are:

$$[\sigma] = \frac{[q]}{[S]} = \frac{\text{sec} \cdot \text{amp}}{\text{m}^2} = \text{m}^{-2} \cdot \text{sec} \cdot \text{amp}$$

Potential (voltage, emf). The unit of potential is determined from the equation:

$$W = kqU$$

from which:

$$U = \frac{1}{k}\frac{W}{q} \tag{5.3}$$

where W is the work done by an electric field in moving a charge q through a potential difference of U.

Assuming, in Eq. (5.3), that $k = 1$, $W = 1$ J, and $q = 1$ coulomb, we find that:

$$1 \text{ unit of potential } = 1 \cdot \frac{1 \text{ J}}{1 \text{ coulomb}} = 1\frac{\text{J}}{\text{coulomb}}$$

This unit is called a volt.

A volt (v) is the potential difference between two points that requires 1 joule of work to move a charge of 1 coulomb from one of the points to the other.

Table 7

Units of Measurement of Electric and Magnetic Quantities in the MKSA System

Name of quantity	Fundamental equation	Unit of measurement		
		Name	Abbreviation	Dimensions
Charge	$q = It$	coulomb (ampere-second)	none	$sec \cdot amp$
Surface charge density	$\sigma = \dfrac{q}{S}$	—	—	$m^{-2} \cdot sec \cdot amp$
Potential (voltage, emf)	$U = \dfrac{W}{q}$	volt	v	$m^{2} \cdot kg \cdot sec^{-3} \cdot amp^{-1}$
Capacitance	$C = \dfrac{q}{U}$	farad	f	$m^{-2} \cdot kg^{-1} \cdot sec^{4} \cdot amp^{2}$
Resistance	$R = \dfrac{U}{I}$	ohm	Ω	$m^{2} \cdot kg \cdot sec^{-3} \cdot amp^{-2}$
Electric field intensity	$E = \dfrac{U}{d}$	volt/meter	v/m	$m \cdot kg \cdot sec^{-3} \cdot amp^{-1}$
Dielectric permittivity	$\epsilon = \dfrac{4\pi dC}{S}$	farad/meter	f/m	$m^{-3} \cdot kg^{-1} \cdot sec^{4} \cdot amp^{2}$
Electric displacement	$D = \epsilon E$	coulomb/meter^2	none	$m^{-2} \cdot sec \cdot amp$
Electric induction flux	$N = 4\pi q$	coulomb (ampere-second)	—	$sec \cdot amp$
Magnetic induction flux (magnetic flux)	$d\Phi = -E_i dt$	weber (volt-second)	—	$m^{2} \cdot kg \cdot sec^{-2} \cdot amp^{-1}$

Quantity	Equation	Unit	Symbol	Dimensions
Flux linkage	$\Psi = \Phi N$	weber (volt-second)	—	$m^2 \cdot kg \cdot sec^{-2} \cdot amp^{-1}$
Magnetic induction (magnetic flux density)	$B = \dfrac{\Phi}{S}$	weber/meter^2	—	$kg \cdot sec^{-2} \cdot amp^{-1}$
Magnetic field intensity	$H = \dfrac{2I}{r}$	amp/meter	amp/m	$m^{-1} \cdot amp$
Magnetic moment	$p_m = \dfrac{M}{H}$	—	—	$m^3 \cdot kg \cdot sec^{-2} \cdot amp^{-1}$
Magnetic mass (amount of magnetism)	$m = \dfrac{p_m}{l}$	—	—	$m^2 \cdot kg \cdot sec^{-2} \cdot amp^{-1}$
Magnetomotive force	$E_m = 4\pi nI$	ampere-turns	—	amp
Inductance	$L = \dfrac{\Psi}{I}$	henry	h	$m^2 \cdot kg \cdot sec^{-2} \cdot amp^{-2}$
Magnetic permeability	$\mu = \dfrac{B}{H}$	henry/meter	h/m	$m \cdot kg \cdot sec^{-2} \cdot amp^{-2}$

The unit of potential can also be determined from the equation:

$$P = kIU$$

where P is the power generated in a conductor by a current I when a voltage U exists between the terminals of the conductor. From this equation we find:

$$U = \frac{1}{k} \frac{P}{I} \tag{5.4}$$

Assuming here that $k = 1$, $P = 1$ watt, and $I = 1$ amp, we obtain:

$$1 \text{ v} = 1 \cdot \frac{1 \text{ watt}}{1 \text{ amp}} = 1 \frac{\text{watt}}{\text{amp}}$$

On the basis of Eq. (5.4), the volt can be defined as the potential difference between the terminals of a conductor carrying 1 ampere of current and generating a power of 1 watt.

The dimensions of the volt can be determined from Eq. (5.3):

$$[U] = \frac{[W]}{[q]} = \frac{\text{m}^2 \cdot \text{kg} \cdot \text{sec}^{-2}}{\text{sec} \cdot \text{amp}} = \text{m}^2 \cdot \text{kg} \cdot \text{sec}^{-3} \cdot \text{amp}^{-1}$$

or from Eq. (5.4):

$$[U] = \frac{[P]}{[I]} = \frac{\text{m}^2 \cdot \text{kg} \cdot \text{sec}^{-3}}{\text{amp}} = \text{m}^2 \cdot \text{kg} \cdot \text{sec}^{-3} \cdot \text{amp}^{-1}$$

Capacitance. The unit of measurement of capacitance C is determined from the equation:

$$C = k \frac{q}{U} \tag{5.5}$$

where U is the potential of the conductor and q is the charge on the conductor.

Assuming, in Eq. (5.5), that $k = 1$, $q = 1$ coulomb, and $U = 1$ v, we obtain:

$$1 \text{ unit of capacitance} = 1 \cdot \frac{1 \text{ coulomb}}{1 \text{ v}} = 1 \frac{\text{coulomb}}{\text{v}}$$

The unit of capacitance is called the *farad.*

A condenser is said to have a capacitance of one farad if a change of potential of one volt results from a charge of one coulomb on the condenser.

The dimensions of the farad are determined from Eq. (5.5):

$$[C] = \frac{[q]}{[U]} = \frac{\text{sec} \cdot \text{amp}}{\text{m}^2 \cdot \text{kg} \cdot \text{sec}^{-3} \cdot \text{amp}^{-1}} = \text{m}^{-2} \cdot \text{kg}^{-1} \cdot \text{sec}^4 \cdot \text{amp}^2$$

Resistance. The unit of resistance is determined from Ohm's law:

$$I = k\frac{U}{R}$$

from which:

$$R = \frac{1}{k}\frac{U}{I} \tag{5.6}$$

where U is the potential difference between the ends of a conductor with resistance R, and I is the current.

Assuming, in (5.6), that $k = 1$, $U = 1$ v, and $I = 1$ amp, we obtain:

$$1 \text{ unit of resistance} = 1 \cdot \frac{1 \text{ v}}{1 \text{ amp}} = 1\frac{\text{v}}{\text{amp}}$$

The unit of resistance is the *ohm*.

The ohm (Ω) is the resistance of a conductor through which a current of 1 ampere passes when the voltage between the terminals of the conductor is 1 volt.

We can determine the dimensions of the ohm from Eq. (5.6):

$$[R] = \frac{[U]}{[I]} = \frac{\text{m}^2 \cdot \text{kg} \cdot \text{sec}^{-3} \cdot \text{amp}^{-1}}{\text{amp}} = \text{m}^2 \cdot \text{kg} \cdot \text{sec}^{-3} \cdot \text{amp}^{-2}$$

Electric field intensity. The unit of electric field intensity is found from the equation:

$$E = k\frac{U}{d} \tag{5.7}$$

which expresses the dependence between the intensity E of a homogeneous electric field and the potential difference U between two points in the field separated by a distance d in the direction of the line of force.

Substituting $k = 1$, $U = 1$ v, and $d = 1$ m, we obtain:

$$1 \text{ unit of field intensity} = 1\frac{1 \text{ v}}{1 \text{ m}} = 1\frac{\text{v}}{\text{m}}$$

The unit of electric field intensity is called the volt per meter.

The volt/meter (v/m) is the intensity of a homogeneous electric field whose potential, along the line of force, changes by 1 v over a distance of 1 m.

The dimensions of the v/m are determined from Eq. (5.7):

$$[E] = \frac{[U]}{[d]} = \frac{m^2 \cdot kg \cdot sec^{-3} \cdot amp^{-1}}{m} = m \cdot kg \cdot sec^{-3} \cdot amp^{-1}$$

Dielectric permittivity. The unit of dielectric permittivity is determined from the equation for the capacitance of a plane condenser:

$$C = \frac{\varepsilon S}{4\pi d}$$

where ε is the dielectric permittivity of the medium which occupies the space between the condenser plates, S is the area of one plate, and d is the distance between the plates.

This formula gives us:

$$\varepsilon = \frac{4\pi d C}{S} \tag{5.8}$$

Assuming that $d = 1$ m, $S = 1$ m^2, and $C = \frac{1}{4\pi}$ f, we get:

1 unit of dielectric permittivity =

$$\frac{4\pi \cdot 1 \text{ m} \cdot \frac{1}{4\pi} \text{ f}}{1 \text{ m}^2} = 1\frac{\text{f}}{\text{m}}$$

This unit is called the farad per meter.

The farad/meter (f/m) is the dielectric permittivity of a dielectric which, filling the space between two condenser plates of area 1 m^2 each and separated by 1 m, acquires a capacitance of $\frac{1}{4\pi}$ f on the condenser.

The dimensions of the f/m are determined from Eq. (5.8):

$$[\varepsilon] = \frac{[d][C]}{[S]} = \frac{m \cdot m^{-2} \cdot kg^{-1} \cdot sec^4 \cdot amp^2}{m^2} = m^{-3} \cdot kg^{-1} \cdot sec^4 \cdot amp^2$$

When operating with equations containing the dielectric permittivity ε, it should be remembered that in physics, as well as in electrical engineering, a medium is generally described by relative permittivity rather than by actual permittivity.

The relative dielectric permittivity of a medium is the ratio of the actual permittivity of the medium ε to the dielectric permittivity of a vacuum ε_0, that is:

$$\varepsilon_r = \frac{\varepsilon}{\varepsilon_0} \tag{5.9}$$

whence the actual dielectric permittivity of a medium is found to be:

$$\varepsilon = \varepsilon_r \cdot \varepsilon_0 \tag{5.10}$$

When using formulas containing the dielectric permittivity, it is often necessary to substitute for ε the expression in Eq. (5.10).

Here ε_r is taken from reference tables. As follows from Eq. (5.10), ε_r is a dimensionless number.

The numerical value and dimensions of the dielectric permittivity of a vacuum (the dielectric constant ε_0) in the MKS system can be derived from Coulomb's law:

$$F = \frac{q_1 \cdot q_2}{\varepsilon_0 r^2} \tag{5.11}$$

where F is the force of interaction between the charges q_1 and q_2 separated by a distance r in a vacuum.

It has been established experimentally that two charges of 1 coulomb each 1 meter apart interact in a vacuum with a force $F = 9 \cdot 10^9$ N.

Substituting $q_1 = q_2 = 1$ coulomb, $r = 1$ m, and $F = 9 \cdot 10^9$ N into (5.11), we obtain:

$$9 \cdot 10^9 \text{ N} = \frac{1 \text{ coulomb} \cdot 1 \text{ coulomb}}{\varepsilon_0 \cdot 1 \text{ m}^2}$$

from which:

$$\varepsilon_0 = \frac{1}{9 \cdot 10^9} \frac{\text{coulomb} \cdot \text{coulomb}}{\text{N} \cdot \text{m}^2}$$

But:

$$\frac{\text{coulomb} \cdot \text{coulomb}}{\text{N} \cdot \text{m}^2} = \frac{\text{coulomb} \cdot \text{coulomb}}{\text{J} \cdot \text{m}} = \frac{\text{coulomb}}{\dfrac{\text{J}}{\text{coulomb}} \cdot \text{m}} = \frac{\text{coulomb}}{\text{v} \cdot \text{m}} = \frac{\text{f}}{\text{m}}$$

Consequently, $\varepsilon_0 = \dfrac{1}{9 \cdot 10^9} \dfrac{\text{f}}{\text{m}} \approx 1.1 \cdot 10^{-10} \dfrac{\text{f}}{\text{m}}$.

Looking ahead for a moment, we should point out that the numerical values and dimensions of the dielectric constant are different in different systems of units (see Appendix 1, Table 18), whereas the relative dielectric permittivity for a given medium is the same in all systems of units.

Electric displacement of an electric field. The unit of measurement of displacement D of an electric field is determined from the equation:

$$D = \varepsilon E = \varepsilon_r \varepsilon_0 E \tag{5.12}$$

Assuming that $E = 1$ v/m, $\varepsilon_0 = 1/(9 \cdot 10^9)$ f/m, and $\varepsilon_r = 9 \cdot 10^9$, we obtain:

$$1 \text{ unit of displacement } =$$

$$9 \cdot 10^9 \cdot \frac{1}{9 \cdot 10^9} \frac{f}{m} \cdot 1 \frac{v}{m} = 1 \frac{f \cdot v}{m^2} = 1 \frac{coulomb}{m^2}$$

The unit of displacement is the coulomb per square meter.

The coulomb/square meter (coulomb/m^2) is the electric displacement of an electric field with an intensity of 1 v/m in a medium whose relative dielectric permittivity is $9 \cdot 10^9$.

The dimensions of the coulomb/m^2 are found from Eq. (5.12):

$$[D] = [i][E] = (m^{-3} \cdot kg^{-1} \cdot sec^4 \cdot amp^2)(m \cdot kg \cdot sec^{-3} \cdot amp^{-1})$$
$$= m^{-2} \cdot sec \cdot amp$$

Electric induction flux   (Electric displacement flux).   The unit of electric induction flux can be determined from the Ostrogradskiy-Gauss theorem:

$$N = k4\pi q \tag{5.13}$$

where N is the electric induction flux permeating an enclosed surface which contains a charge q.

This formula means that the induction flux is measured in coulombs or ampere-seconds. The dimensions of the unit are sec · amp.

The ampere-second (amp · sec) is the electric induction flux created by a charge of $(1/4\pi)$ coulomb.

Magnetic induction flux (magnetic flux). The units of the magnetic flux and the flux linkage are determined by the Faraday-Maxwell law:

$$E_i = -k \frac{d\Psi}{dt} \tag{5.14}$$

where E_i is the emf (electromotive force) of the induction created in a closed circuit (loop) and $d\Psi$ is the change in the magnetic flux permeating the loop in the time dt.

Flux linkage. The flux linkage is the quantity numerically equal to the product of Φ, the magnetic flux through the cross section of a solenoid, and N, the number of turns in the solenoid; that is, $\Psi = \Phi N$. In some textbooks, both the magnetic flux and the flux linkage are designated by the same letter—Φ—which may cause some misunderstanding in the solution of problems. We advise the reader to distinguish clearly between these quantities. When calculating the inductance of a solenoid, it is not the magnetic flux but the flux linkage which should be considered, and the equation $\Psi = LI$ should be used. This gives us $L = \frac{\Psi}{I} = \frac{\Phi N}{I}$. The magnetic flux and the flux linkage coincide for a solenoid containing one turn.

The flux linkage is measured in the same units as the magnetic flux. It follows from Eq. (5.14) that:

$$d\Psi = -\frac{1}{k} E_i dt \tag{5.15}$$

Substituting $k = 1$, $E_i = 1$ v, and $dt = 1$ sec into (5.15), we find that:

$$1 \text{ MKSA } (\Psi) = 1 \text{ v} \cdot 1 \text{ sec} = 1 \text{ v} \cdot \text{sec}$$

This unit is called the volt-second or the *weber*.

The weber is the magnetic flux which, as it decreases to zero in 1 sec, induces an emf of 1 volt in a loop linked to the flux.

The weber can be also determined from the formula:

$$q = \frac{\Delta \Psi}{R}$$

where q is the amount of electricity flowing through a nonbranching circuit with resistance R, with a variation in the magnetic flux linked to this circuit of $\Delta \Psi$.

This equation gives us:

$$\Delta \Psi = qR \tag{5.16}$$

On the basis of Eq. (5.16), the weber can be defined as follows.

The weber is the magnetic flux which, as it decreases to zero, produces one coulomb of electricity flowing through an unbranching circuit of resistance 1 ohm linked to the flux.

The dimensions of the magnetic flux can be determined either from Eq. (5.15):

$$[d\Psi] = [E_i][dt] = \text{m}^2 \cdot \text{kg} \cdot \text{sec}^{-3} \cdot \text{amp}^{-1} \cdot \text{sec} = \text{m}^2 \cdot \text{kg} \cdot \text{sec}^{-2} \cdot \text{amp}^{-1}$$

or from Eq. (5.16):

$$[d\Psi] = [q][R] = \text{sec} \cdot \text{amp} \cdot \text{m}^2 \cdot \text{kg} \cdot \text{sec}^{-3} \cdot \text{amp}^{-2}$$
$$= \text{m}^2 \cdot \text{kg} \cdot \text{sec}^{-2} \cdot \text{amp}^{-1}$$

Magnetic induction (magnetic flux density). The unit of magnetic induction is determined from the equation:

$$B = k \frac{\Phi}{S} \tag{5.17}$$

where B is the induction of a homogeneous magnetic field and Φ is the magnetic flux permeating the area S. Assuming, in Eq. (5.17), that $k = 1$, $\Phi = 1$ weber, and $S = 1$ m^2, we obtain:

$$1 \text{ unit of induction} = 1 \cdot \frac{1 \text{ weber}}{1 \text{ m}^2} = 1 \frac{\text{weber}}{\text{m}^2}$$

This unit is termed the weber per square meter.

The weber per square meter (weber/m²) is the induction of a homogeneous magnetic field in which the magnetic flux through an area of 1 m² (perpendicular to the direction of the field) is equal to 1 weber.

The dimensions of the weber per square meter are:

$$[B] = \frac{[\Phi]}{[S]} = \frac{m^2 \cdot kg \cdot sec^{-2} \cdot amp^{-1}}{m^2} = kg \cdot sec^{-2} \cdot amp^{-1}$$

Magnetic field intensity. The unit of magnetic field intensity is determined from the equation:

$$H = k \frac{2I}{r} \tag{5.18}$$

which expresses the intensity of a magnetic field H at a point a distance r away from a rectilinear, infinitely long current I which creates the field.

Assuming, in (5.18), that $k = 1$, $I = 1$ amp and $r = 2$ m, we obtain:

$$1 \text{ MKSA } (H) = 1 \cdot \frac{1 \text{ amp}}{1 \text{ m}} = 1 \frac{amp}{m}$$

This unit is called the ampere per meter.

The ampere/meter (amp/m) is the intensity of the magnetic field created by a rectilinear, infinitely long current of 1 amp at a distance of 2 m from the current-carrying conductor.

As follows from Eq. (5.18), the dimensions of this unit of intensity are $m^{-1} \cdot amp$.

Magnetic moment. The unit of magnetic moment is determined from the equation:

$$M = k p_m H \sin \alpha$$

where p_m is the magnetic moment of a magnet or a current-carrying circuit, M is the mechanical moment acting on the magnet or circuit when placed in a uniform magnetic field with intensity H, and α is the angle between the direction of the field and the magnet's axis (normal to the plane of the coil).

This formula gives us:

$$p_m = \frac{1}{k} \frac{M}{H \sin \alpha} \tag{5.19}$$

Assuming, in this formula, that $k = 1$, $H = 1$ amp/m, $M = 1$ N·m, and $\alpha = 90°$, we obtain:

$$1 \text{ MKSA } (p_m) = 1 \cdot \frac{1 \text{ N} \cdot \text{m}}{1 \frac{amp}{m}} = 1 \frac{\text{N} \cdot \text{m}}{\frac{amp}{m}}$$

The unit of magnetic moment in the MKSA system is taken as the magnetic moment of a permanent magnet (or a current-carrying coil) acted on by a maximal rotational moment of 1 N · m in a uniform magnetic field.

The dimensions of the unit of magnetic moment are:

$$[p_m] = \frac{[M]}{[H]} = \frac{\text{kg} \cdot \text{m} \cdot \text{m} \cdot \text{m}}{\text{sec}^2 \cdot \text{amp}} = \text{m}^3 \cdot \text{kg} \cdot \text{sec}^{-2} \cdot \text{amp}^{-1}$$

Magnetic mass. The unit of magnetic mass is determined from the equation:

$$p_m = kml$$

where m is the magnetic mass of the pole and l is the distance between the poles of a magnet possessing a magnetic moment p_m.

We find from this equation that:

$$m = \frac{1}{k} \frac{p_m}{l} \tag{5.20}$$

Assuming, in this equation, that $k = 1$, $p_m = 1$ MKSA (p_m), and $l = 1$ m, we obtain:

$$1 \text{ MKSA } (m) = \frac{1 \text{ MKSA } (p_m)}{\text{m}}$$

The unit of magnetic mass in the MKSA system is taken as the magnetic mass of a pole of a magnet which possesses one unit of magnetic moment when its length is 1 m. This unit does not have a special name.

The dimensions of the unit of magnetic mass are:

$$[m] = \frac{[p_m]}{[l]} = \frac{\text{m}^3 \cdot \text{kg} \cdot \text{sec}^{-2} \cdot \text{amp}^{-1}}{\text{m}} = \text{m}^2 \cdot \text{kg} \cdot \text{sec}^{-2} \cdot \text{amp}^{-1}$$

Magnetomotive force. The unit of magnetomotive force is determined by the equation:

$$E_m = k \frac{A}{m} = k \frac{4\pi mnI}{m} = 4k\pi nI \tag{5.21}$$

where A is the work done when the magnetic pole m passes around a closed magnetic circuit and E_m is the magnetomotive force (that is, the work done when a unit north pole passes around an unbranched closed circuit formed by n coils carrying a current I).

It follows from (5.21) that the magnetomotive force is measured in units with the dimension of current: amperes. This unit is called the *ampere-turn.*

The ampere-turn (amp-turn) is the magnetomotive force created in one turn carrying a current of $(1/4\,\pi)$ amp.

Inductance of a circuit. The unit of inductance of a circuit is determined from the equation:

$$\Psi = kLI$$

where Ψ is the flux linkage, that is, the magnetic flux linked to the circuit when a current I is flowing through it, and L is the inductance of the circuit. L is numerically equal to the magnetic flux linked to the circuit when one unit of current is flowing through it.

It follows from this formula that:

$$L = \frac{1}{k}\frac{\Psi}{I} \tag{5.22}$$

Assuming, in (5.22), that $k = 1$, $\Psi = 1$ weber, and $I = 1$ amp, we obtain:

$$1 \text{ unit of inductance} = 1 \cdot \frac{1 \text{ weber}}{1 \text{ amp}} = 1\frac{\text{weber}}{\text{amp}}$$

This unit is called the *henry.*

The henry (h) is the inductance of a circuit which is linked to a magnetic flux of 1 weber when a current of 1 amp flows through it.

The unit of inductance can also be determined from the Faraday-Maxwell law applied to the emf of self-inductance:

$$E_i = -k\frac{d\Psi}{dt} = -k\frac{d(LI)}{dt} = -kL\frac{dI}{dt}$$

It follows from this equation that:

$$L = -\frac{1}{k}\frac{E_i}{\frac{dI}{dt}} \tag{5.23}$$

that is, the inductance is numerically equal to the emf of self-inductance created in the circuit when the current varies at a rate of 1 unit of current per unit of time.

Assuming, in (5.23), that $k = 1$, $E_i = 1$ v, and $dI/dt = 1$ amp/sec, we find that:

$$1 \text{ unit of inductance} = 1 \cdot \frac{1 \text{ v}}{1\frac{\text{amp}}{\text{sec}}} = 1\frac{\text{v} \cdot \text{sec}}{\text{amp}}$$

In accordance with the Faraday-Maxwell law, the henry can be defined as follows.

The henry is the inductance of a circuit in which a self-induced emf of 1 volt is created when the current in the circuit varies at a rate of 1 amp per second.

The dimensions of the henry can also be determined from Eq. (5.22):

$$[L] = \frac{[\Psi]}{[I]} = \frac{m^2 \cdot kg \cdot sec^{-2} \cdot amp^{-1}}{amp} = m^2 \cdot kg \cdot sec^{-2} \cdot amp^{-2}$$

or from (5.23):

$$[L] = \frac{[E_i]}{\left[\frac{dI}{dt}\right]} = \frac{m^2 \cdot kg \cdot sec^{-3} \cdot amp^{-1}}{sec^{-1} \cdot amp} = m^2 \cdot kg \cdot sec^{-2} \cdot amp^{-2}$$

Magnetic permeability. The unit of magnetic permeability is obtained from the formula:

$$\mu = k\frac{B}{H} \tag{5.24}$$

Assuming, in (5.24), that $k = 1$, $B = 1$ weber/m², and $H = 1$ amp/m, we find that:

$$1 \text{ MKSA } (\mu) = 1 \cdot \frac{1\dfrac{weber}{m^2}}{1\dfrac{amp}{m}} = 1\frac{\dfrac{weber}{amp}}{m} = 1\frac{h}{m}$$

This unit is called the henry per meter.

The henry/meter (h/m) is the magnetic permeability of a substance in which the magnetic field intensity is equal to 1 amp/m at an induction of 1 weber/m².

When using formulas containing magnetic permeability μ, it is vital to keep the following fact in mind. In both physics and electrical engineering, a medium is usually described by its relative magnetic permeability, rather than its actual permeability. The former is a ratio of the actual magnetic permeability μ to the magnetic permeability in a vacuum μ_0, that is:

$$\mu_r = \frac{\mu}{\mu_0}$$

Since μ and μ_0 are measured in h/m, μ_r is a dimensionless number. When making calculations, we substitute the following for μ:

$$\mu = \mu_r \mu_0$$

Here μ_r is taken from reference tables, or, in the case of ferromagnetic materials, is determined from graphs showing the induction B as a function of the magnetic field intensity H.

The magnetic permeability of a vacuum or the magnetic constant μ_0 is determined from Coulomb's law as applied to the interaction between magnetic poles in a vacuum:

$$F = \frac{m_1 m_2}{\mu_0 r^2} \qquad (5.25)$$

Experimental data show that two magnetic poles, each with one unit of magnetic mass in the MKSA system, interact at a distance of 1 m with a force of $F = 10^7$ N.

Determining μ_0 from (5.25), and substituting the numerical values $F = 10^7$ N, $r = 1$ m, $m_1 = m_2 = m = 1$ m$^2 \cdot$ kg $\cdot$ sec$^{-2} \cdot$ amp^{-1}, we obtain:

$$\mu_0 = \frac{m^2}{Fr^2} = \frac{(1 \text{ m}^2 \cdot \text{kg} \cdot \text{sec}^{-2} \cdot \text{amp}^{-1})^2}{10^7 \text{ N} \cdot 1 \text{ m}^2}$$

$$= 10^{-7} \frac{\text{m}^4 \cdot \text{kg}^2 \cdot \text{sec}^{-4} \cdot \text{amp}^{-2}}{\text{kg} \cdot \text{m} \cdot \text{sec}^{-2} \cdot \text{m}^2} = 10^{-7} \frac{\text{m}^2 \cdot \text{kg} \cdot \text{sec}^{-2} \cdot \text{amp}^{-2}}{\text{m}}$$

or:

$$\mu_0 = 10^{-7} \frac{\text{h}}{\text{m}}$$

In other systems of units, the numerical value and the dimensions of the magnetic constant μ_0 are different (see Appendix 1, Table 18). However, the numerical value of the relative magnetic permeability of a given medium is the same in all systems of measurement.

2. THE CGS ESU SYSTEM

The cgs esu system* is based on the cgs system for mechanical quantities. Hence the fundamental units in the cgs esu system are as follows:

The centimeter (cm)—the unit of length;

The gram (g)—the unit of mass;

The second (sec)—the unit of time.

The fourth fundamental unit is the *electric constant* ε_0, the unit of measurement of dielectric permittivity of a medium.

As a fundamental unit, ε_0 should be contained in the dimensions of all the derived units of the cgs esu system.

For the sake of simplicity, however, the electric constant ε_0 in the cgs esu system is taken as a dimensionless quantity equal to unity. Such a choice is possible since the fundamental unit is selected arbitrarily. This simplifies considerably the dimensions of units of

---

*The letters esu denote "electrostatic unit."

measurement in the cgs esu system; that is, all the derived electric and magnetic units are expressed in terms of cm, g, and sec.

This choice of the electric constant ε_0 is the principal characteristic of the cgs esu system and distinguishes it from the cgs emu system, which is also based on the cgs system.

To construct the cgs esu system (to determine its derived units), we have to express the electromagnetic equations in a series satisfying the conditions presented in Chapter I. The series in Table 8 satisfies these conditions.

The fundamental equations in this table enable us to determine, successively, the derived units in the cgs esu system.

Charge (amount of electricity). The initial equation in constructing the cgs esu system is Coulomb's law:

$$F = k \frac{q_1 q_2}{\varepsilon r^2}$$

If we express the dielectric permittivity in terms of the dielectric constant ε_0 (cf. Eq. 5.10), this equation takes the form:

$$F = k \frac{q_1 q_2}{\varepsilon_r \varepsilon_0 r^2} \tag{5.26}$$

Equation (5.26) enables us to define the unit of charge in the cgs esu system. To do this, let us consider the interaction of two identical charges $q_1 = q_2 = q$ separated by a distance of 1 centimeter in a vacuum. We can then assume that $\varepsilon_r = 1$, since the relative dielectric permittivity of a vacuum is equal to unity in all systems; $\varepsilon_0 = 1$, since, in the cgs esu system, the dielectric constant is taken as unity and $r = 1$ cm—as agreed.

Substituting these values of ε_r, ε_0, and r into Eq. (5.26) we obtain:

$$F = kq^2$$

As the unit of charge let us take the charge that, for $k = 1$, results in a force equal to 1 dyne.

The unit of charge selected in this way is called the statcoulomb.

The statcoulomb is the charge which interacts in a vacuum with an equal charge (of 1 statcoulomb) at a distance of 1 cm with a force of 1 dyne.

The dimensions of the unit of charge in the cgs esu system are found from Eq. (5.26). Expressing q in terms of the remaining quantities, we obtain:

$$q = \sqrt{\varepsilon_r \varepsilon_0 F r^2}$$

Remembering that ε_0, in the cgs esu esystem, and ε_r (in any system) are dimensionless quantities, we find that:

Table 8

Units of Measurement of Electric and Magnetic Quantities in the cgs esu System

Name of quantity	Fundamental equation	Unit of measurement		
		Name	Abbreviation	Dimensions
Charge (amount of electricity)	$q = r\sqrt{F}$	stat-coulomb	cgs esu (q)	$cm^{3/2} \cdot g^{1/2} \cdot sec^{-1}$
Surface charge density	$\sigma = \dfrac{q}{S}$	—	cgs esu (σ)	$cm^{-1/2} \cdot g^{1/2} \cdot sec^{-1}$
Electric field intensity	$E = \dfrac{F}{q}$	—	cgs esu (E)	$cm^{-1/2} \cdot g^{1/2} \cdot sec^{-1}$
Electric induction (displacement)	$D = \epsilon E$	—	cgs esu (D)	$cm^{-1/2} \cdot g^{1/2} \cdot sec^{-1}$
Electric induction flux	$N = DS$	—	cgs esu (N)	$cm^{3/2} \cdot g^{1/2} \cdot sec^{-1}$
Potential (voltage, emf)	$U = \dfrac{W}{q}$	statvolt	cgs esu (U)	$cm^{1/2} \cdot g^{1/2} \cdot sec^{-1}$
Dipole moment	$p = ql$	—	cgs esu (p)	$cm^{5/2} \cdot g^{1/2} \cdot sec^{-1}$
Capacitance	$C = \dfrac{q}{U}$	centi-meter	cm	cm
Current	$I = \dfrac{q}{t}$	stat-ampere	cgs esu (I)	$cm^{3/2} \cdot g^{1/2} \cdot sec^{-2}$
Resistance	$R = \dfrac{U}{I}$	statohm	cgs esu (R)	$cm^{-1} \cdot sec$
Magnetic field intensity	$H = \dfrac{2I}{r}$	stat-oersted	cgs esu (H)	$cm^{1/2} \cdot g^{1/2} \cdot sec^{-2}$
Amount of magnetism (magnetic mass)	$m = \dfrac{F}{H}$	—	cgs esu (m)	$cm^{1/2} \cdot g^{1/2}$
Magnetic permeability	$\mu = \dfrac{m_1 \cdot m_2}{F \cdot r^2}$	—	cgs esu (μ)	$cm^{-2} \cdot sec^{2}$
Magnetic induction	$B = \mu \cdot H$	—	cgs esu (B)	$cm^{-3/2} \cdot g^{1/2}$
Magnetic flux	$\Phi = B \cdot S$	—	cgs esu (Φ)	$cm^{1/2} \cdot g^{1/2}$
Flux linkage	$\Psi = \Phi N$	—	cgs esu (Ψ)	$cm^{1/2} \cdot g^{1/2}$
Magnetic moment	$p_m = m \cdot l$	—	cgs esu (p_m)	$cm^{3/2} \cdot g^{1/2}$
Magnetomotive force	$E_m = 4\pi In$	—	cgs esu (E_m)	$cm^{3/2} \cdot g^{1/2} \cdot sec^{-2}$
Magnetic resistance	$R_m = \dfrac{l}{\mu S}$	—	cgs esu (R_m)	$cm \cdot sec^{-2}$
Inductance (coefficient of self-inductance)	$L = \dfrac{\Psi}{I}$	stat-henry	cgs esu (L)	$cm^{-1} \cdot sec^{2}$

$$[q] = \sqrt{[F][r^2]} = \sqrt{cm \cdot g \cdot sec^{-2} \cdot cm^2} = cm^{3/2} \cdot g^{1/2} \cdot sec^{-1}$$

Names of units in the cgs esu system are often formed by placing the prefix stat- before the name of the corresponding unit in the MKSA or cgs emu systems (for example, statcoulomb). We may also designate these units by the abbreviation of the system, followed by the symbol for the quantity, in parentheses [for example, 1 statcoulomb = 1 cgs esu (q)].

Surface charge density. The unit of surface charge density is determined from the equation:

$$\sigma = k \frac{q}{S} \tag{5.27}$$

Assuming, in this equation, that $k = 1$, $q = 1$ cgs esu (q), and $S = 1$ cm^2, we find that:

$$1 \text{ cgs esu } (\sigma) = 1 \cdot \frac{\text{cgs esu } (q)}{1 \text{ cm}^2} = 1 \frac{\text{cgs esu } (q)}{\text{cm}^2} = 1 \frac{\text{statcoulomb}}{\text{cm}^2}$$

The unit of surface charge density in the cgs esu system is taken as the density at which a charge of 1 statcoulomb is uniformly distributed over an area of 1 cm^2.

The dimensions of the surface charge density are:

$$[\sigma] = \frac{[q]}{[S]} = \frac{\text{cm}^{3/2} \cdot \text{g}^{1/2} \cdot \text{sec}^{-1}}{\text{cm}^2} = \text{cm}^{-1/2} \cdot \text{g}^{1/2} \cdot \text{sec}^{-1}$$

Electric field intensity. The unit of electric field intensity is determined from the equation:

$$E = k \frac{F}{q} \tag{5.28}$$

where E is the field intensity (expressing the force acting on a unit positive charge at a given point in the field) and F is the force acting on a charge q in the field.

Substituting $k = 1$, $F = 1$ dyne, and $q = 1$ cgs esu (q) into this equation, we obtain:

$$1 \text{ cgs esu } (E) = 1 \cdot \frac{1 \text{ dyne}}{1 \text{ cgs esu } (q)} = \frac{\text{dyne}}{\text{cgs esu } (q)} = 1 \frac{\text{dyne}}{\text{statcoulomb}}$$

The dyne/statcoulomb is taken as the intensity of a uniform field which exerts a force of 1 dyne on a charge of 1 statcoulomb.

From Eq. (5.28) we can also find the dimensions of the unit of intensity in the cgs esu system:

$$[E] = \frac{[F]}{[q]} = \frac{\text{cm} \cdot \text{g} \cdot \text{sec}^{-2}}{\text{cm}^{3/2} \cdot \text{g}^{1/2} \cdot \text{sec}^{-1}} = \text{cm}^{-1/2} \cdot \text{g}^{1/2} \cdot \text{sec}^{-1}$$

Electric induction (displacement). The unit of displacement D is determined from the equation:

$$D = \varepsilon E \tag{5.29}$$

It is clear from this formula that the displacement of the field should be measured in the same units as the intensity, since the dielectric permittivity ε is a dimensionless quantity in the cgs esu system.

Electric induction flux. The unit of electric induction flux is determined from the equation:

$$N = kDS \qquad (5.30)$$

where N is the induction flux through an area S.

Assuming, in this formula, that $k = 1$, $D = 1$ cgs esu (D), and $S = 1$ cm^2, we find that:

1 cgs esu (N) = 1 cgs esu (D) · 1 cm^2 = 1 cgs esu (D) · cm^2

The unit of electric induction flux in the cgs esu system is taken as the induction flux permeating an area of 1 cm (perpendicular to the field) in a uniform electric field with an induction equal to 1 cgs esu (D).

It follows from Eq. (5.30) that the dimensions of the unit of flux are:

$$[N] = [D][S] = \text{cm}^{-1/2} \cdot \text{g}^{1/2} \cdot \text{sec}^{-1} \cdot \text{cm}^2 =$$
$$= \text{cm}^{3/2} \cdot \text{g}^{1/2} \cdot \text{sec}^{-1}$$

Potential (voltage, emf). The unit of potential is determined from the formula:

$$U = k\frac{W}{q} \qquad (5.31)$$

Assuming, in this formula, that $k = 1$, $W = 1$ erg, and $q = 1$ cgs esu (q), we find that:

1 cgs esu (U) = 1 · $\dfrac{1 \text{ erg}}{1 \text{ cgs esu } (q)}$ = 1 $\dfrac{\text{erg}}{\text{cgs esu } (q)}$

The unit of potential in the cgs esu system is called the *statvolt*.

The statvolt is taken as the potential at a point in a field in which 1 erg of work is done when a charge of 1 statcoulomb is moved from that point to infinity.

The statvolt can also be determined from formula:

$$\Delta U = kEd \qquad (5.32)$$

which expresses the relationship between the potential U and the voltage E of a homogeneous electric field.

In this formula, U is the change in potential over a distance d, taken along a line of force of the field. Assuming, in (5.32), that $k = 1$, $E = 1$ cgs esu (E) and $d = 1$ cm, we find that:

$$1 \text{ cgs esu } (U) = 1 \text{ cgs esu } (E) \cdot 1 \text{ cm}$$

that is, the unit of potential in the cgs esu system is taken as the change in the potential over a distance of 1 cm (along a line of force) of a homogeneous electrostatic field with an intensity of 1 cgs esu (E).

The dimensions of the unit of potential in the cgs esu system can be determined from Eq. (5.31):

$$[U] = \frac{[W]}{[q]} = \frac{\text{cm}^2 \cdot \text{g} \cdot \text{sec}^{-2}}{\text{cm}^{3/2} \cdot \text{g}^{1/2} \cdot \text{sec}^{-1}} = \text{cm}^{1/2} \cdot \text{g}^{1/2} \cdot \text{sec}^{-1}$$

or from Eq. (5.32):

$$[U] = [E][d] = \text{cm}^{-1/2} \cdot \text{g}^{1/2} \cdot \text{sec}^{-1} \cdot \text{cm} = \text{cm}^{1/2} \cdot \text{g}^{1/2} \cdot \text{sec}^{-1}$$

Dipole moment. The unit of dipole moment p is found from the equation:

$$p = kql \tag{5.33}$$

where q is the magnitude of each of the dipole charges and l is the distance between them.

Assuming, in (5.33), that $k = 1$, $q = 1$ cgs esu (q), and $l = 1$ cm, we find that:

$$1 \text{ cgs esu } (p) = 1 \text{ cgs esu } (q) \cdot 1 \text{ cm} = 1 \text{ cgs esu } (q) \cdot \text{cm}$$

The unit of dipole moment in the cgs esu system is taken as the dipole moment of two charges of 1 cgs esu (q) each separated by a distance of 1 cm.

It follows from (5.33) that the dimensions of the unit of dipole moment are:

$$[p] = [q][l] = \text{cm}^{3/2} \cdot \text{g}^{1/2} \cdot \text{sec}^{-1} \cdot \text{cm} = \text{cm}^{5/2} \cdot \text{g}^{1/2} \cdot \text{sec}^{-1}$$

Capacitance. The unit of capacitance C is determined from the equation:

$$C = k \frac{q}{U} \tag{5.34}$$

where U is the potential acquired by a condenser when it has accumulated a charge q.

Assuming, in (5.34), that $k = 1$, $q = 1$ cgs esu (q), and $U = 1$ cgs esu (U), we obtain:

$$1 \text{ cgs esu } (C) = \frac{1 \text{ cgs esu } (q)}{1 \text{ cgs esu } (U)} = 1 \frac{\text{statcoulomb}}{\text{statvolt}}$$

This unit is called the *centimeter*.

The centimeter (cm) is the capacitance of a condenser whose potential is increased by 1 statvolt when it accumulates an additional statcoulomb of charge.

A spherical condenser of radius 1 cm, in a vacuum, possesses a capacitance of 1 cm.

It follows from (5.34) that the dimensions of the unit of capacitance in the cgs esu system are:

$$[C] = \frac{[q]}{[U]} = \frac{\text{cm}^{3/2} \cdot \text{g}^{1/2} \cdot \text{sec}^{-1}}{\text{cm}^{1/2} \cdot \text{g}^{1/2} \cdot \text{sec}^{-1}} = \text{cm}$$

Current. The unit of current I is determined from the equation:

$$I = k \frac{q}{t} \tag{5.35}$$

where q is the charge passing through a cross section of the conductor in time t.

Assuming, in this formula, that $k = 1$, $q = 1$ cgs esu (q), and $t = 1$ sec, we find that:

$$1 \text{ cgs esu } (I) = 1 \cdot \frac{1 \text{ cgs esu } (q)}{1 \text{ sec}} = 1 \frac{\text{cgs esu } (q)}{\text{sec}}$$

This unit is called the *statampere*.

The statampere is taken as the current at which a charge of 1 statcoulomb passes through the cross section of a conductor in 1 sec.

Equation (5.35) gives us the dimensions of the unit of current:

$$[I] = \frac{[q]}{[t]} = \frac{\text{cm}^{3/2} \cdot \text{g}^{1/2} \cdot \text{sec}^{-1}}{\text{sec}} = \text{cm}^{3/2} \cdot \text{g}^{1/2} \cdot \text{sec}^{-2}$$

Resistance. The unit of resistance is determined by the equation:

$$R = k \frac{U}{I} \tag{5.36}$$

Assuming, in this equation, that $k = 1$, $U = 1$ cgs esu (U), and $I = 1$ cgs esu (I), we find that:

$$1 \text{ cgs esu } (R) = 1 \cdot \frac{1 \text{ cgs esu } (U)}{1 \text{ cgs esu } (I)} = 1 \frac{\text{statvolt}}{\text{statampere}}$$

The unit of resistance in the cgs esu system is called the *statohm*.

The statohm is taken as the resistance of a conductor through which a current of 1 statampere flows when there is a potential difference of 1 statvolt between the ends of the conductor.

The dimensions of the statohm are:

$$[R] = \frac{[U]}{[I]} = \frac{cm^{1/2} \cdot g^{1/2} \cdot sec^{-1}}{cm^{3/2} \cdot g^{1/2} \cdot sec^{-2}} = cm^{-1} \cdot sec$$

The cgs esu system is seldom used in magnetism; hence the units of measurement for magnetic and electromagnetic quantities in the cgs esu system are not given here. They can be found in Table 8.

By using the fundamental equations in the table and the methods developed in this section, the reader may, if the occasion arises, easily derive the dimensions of the magnetic quantities in the cgs esu system.

3. THE CGS EMU SYSTEM

The cgs emu system is based on the cgs system for mechanical units. Accordingly, the fundamental units in the cgs emu system are as follows:

The centimeter (cm)—the unit of length;

The gram (g)—the unit of mass;

The second (sec)—the unit of time.

The unit chosen as the fourth fundamental unit is the *magnetic constant* μ_0, the unit of measurement of the magnetic permeability of a medium.

For purposes of simplification, the magnetic constant μ_0 in the cgs emu system is considered as a dimensionless quantity equal to 1.

The cgs emu system can be formulated in two different ways (that is, the units of measurement of the derived electric and magnetic quantities can be determined in two different ways).

Using the first method, we take Coulomb's law for the interaction of magnetic poles as the initial determining equation:

$$F = k \frac{m_1 \cdot m_2}{\mu r^2} \tag{5.37}$$

where m_1 and m_2 are the magnetic masses of the poles, r is the distance between them, and μ is the magnetic permeability of the medium.

The unit of measurement of magnetic mass is determined from Coulomb's law.

Moreover, using the equation:

$$H = \frac{m}{r^2}$$

(where H is the magnetic field intensity created by the magnetic pole m at a point a distance r from the pole), we determine the unit of magnetic field intensity.

Then the equation:

$$B = \mu H$$

is used to determine the induction B of the magnetic field, etc.

In the second method we take, as the initial fundamental equation, the formula expressing the force F of interaction between two infinitely long, parallel current-carrying conductors:

$$F = k \frac{2\mu I_1 I_2}{r} l \tag{5.38}$$

where I_1 and I_2 are the currents in the conductors, l is the segment of conductor for which the current is being calculated, r is the distance between the conductors, and k is a proportionality constant which depends on the choice of units.

This equation is used to determine the unit of current. Then, using the equation:

$$H = \frac{2I}{r}$$

(which expresses the magnetic field intensity H created by an infinitely long current-carrying wire), we can determine the unit of magnetic field intensity. Next, from the equation:

$$B = \mu H$$

we determine the unit of measurement of magnetic induction B and so on.

From a rigorous point of view, both these methods are equivalent. However, the first method of constructing the cgs emu system is purely formal, since the concept of magnetic mass is a fictitious one, retained in physics solely for the purpose of simplifying the calculation of the interaction between magnetic poles. The second method reflects the true situation, that is, the fact that the magnetic fields are created not by a particular magnetic substance, but by an electric current. Hence, in this book we prefer to use the second method of formulating the system.

In order to determine the derivative units of measurement of electric and magnetic quantities, we express the equations of electromagnetism in a series satisfying the following conditions:

1) the first formula in the series must determine an electric quantity, expressed solely in terms of mechanical quantities;

2) each successive formula in the series must determine a quantity expressed in terms of mechanical quantities and electromagnetic quantities which have already been determined by previous equations in the series.

Table 9

Units of Measurement of Electric and Magnetic Quantities in the cgs emu System

Name of quantity	Funda-mental equation	Unit of measurement		
		Name	Abbreviation	Dimensions
Current	$I = \sqrt{\dfrac{F \cdot r}{l}}$	ab-ampere	cgs emu (I)	$cm^{1/2} \cdot g^{1/2} \cdot sec^{-1}$
Magnetic field intensity	$H = \dfrac{I}{r}$	oersted	oe	$cm^{-1/2} \cdot g^{1/2} \cdot sec^{-1}$
Magnetic induction (magnetic flux density)	$B = \mu H$	gauss	—	$cm^{-1/2} \cdot g^{1/2} \cdot sec^{-1}$
Magnetic induction flux (magnetic flux)	$\Phi = BS$	maxwell	—	$cm^{3/2} \cdot g^{1/2} \cdot sec^{-1}$
Magnetic mass	$m = \dfrac{F \cdot r^2}{I \cdot l}$	—	cgs emu (m)	$cm^{3/2} \cdot g^{1/2} \cdot sec^{-1}$
Magnetic moment	$p_m = ml$	—	cgs emu (p_m)	$cm^{5/2} \cdot g^{1/2} \cdot sec^{-1}$
Amount of electricity (charge)	$q = I \cdot t$	ab-coulomb	cgs emu (q)	$cm^{1/2} \cdot g^{1/2}$
Surface charge density	$\sigma = \dfrac{q}{S}$	—	cgs emu (σ)	$cm^{-3/2} \cdot g^{1/2}$
Electric field intensity	$E = \dfrac{F}{q}$	—	cgs emu (E)	$cm^{1/2} \cdot g^{1/2} \cdot sec^{-2}$
Dielectric permittivity	$\epsilon = \dfrac{q^2}{F \cdot r^2}$	—	cgs emu (ϵ)	$cm^{-2} \cdot sec^2$
Electric induction (displacement)	$D = \epsilon E$	—	cgs emu (D)	$cm^{-3/2} \cdot g^{1/2}$
Electric induction flux	$N = DS$	—	cgs emu (N)	$cm^{1/2} \cdot g^{1/2}$
Potential (voltage, emf)	$U = \dfrac{W}{q}$	abvolt	cgs emu (U)	$cm^{3/2} \cdot g^{1/2} \cdot sec^{-2}$
Capacitance	$C = \dfrac{q}{U}$	abfarad	cgs emu (C)	$cm^{-1} \cdot sec^2$
Resistance	$R = \dfrac{U}{I}$	abohm	cgs emu (R)	$cm \cdot sec^{-1}$
Specific resistance	$\rho = \dfrac{RS}{I}$	—	cgs emu (ρ)	$cm^2 \cdot sec^{-1}$
Inductance (coefficient of self-induction)	$L = \dfrac{\Psi}{I}$	centi-meter	cm	cm

The series of equations shown in Table 9 satisfies these conditions.
By using these formulas as fundamental equations, we can determine, successively, the derived units of measurement of electromagnetic quantities in the cgs emu system.

Current. The unit of current is determined from the equation:

$$I = \sqrt{\frac{Fr}{2kl}} \tag{5.39}$$

where the current is expressed solely in terms of mechanical quantities. This formula can easily be derived from (5.38) by assuming that $I_1 = I_2 = I$, and $\mu = \mu_r \cdot \mu_0 = 1 \cdot 1 = 1$.

Moreoever, assuming $F = 1$, $l = 1$, and $r = 2$, we find that $I = 1$. Therefore it follows that, in the cgs emu system, the unit of current is taken as the current which, when passing through two parallel wires of infinite length and negligible cross section, placed 2 cm apart in a vacuum, causes a force between the wires of 1 dyne per centimeter of wire.

The unit defined in this way is termed the *abampere* and is denoted as cgs emu (*I*).

Equation (5.39) gives us the dimensions of the abampere:

$$[I] = \sqrt{\frac{[F][r]}{[l]}} = \sqrt{\frac{\text{cm} \cdot \text{g} \cdot \text{sec}^{-2} \cdot \text{cm}}{\text{cm}}} = \text{cm}^{1/2} \cdot \text{g}^{1/2} \cdot \text{sec}^{-1}$$

Magnetic field intensity. The unit of magnetic field intensity is determined from the equation:

$$H = k\frac{2I}{r} \tag{5.40}$$

which expresses the intensity H of the magnetic field created by an infinitely long wire carrying a current I, at a distance r from the wire.

Assuming, in (5.40), that $k = 1$, $I = 1$ abampere, and $r = 2$ cm, we obtain:

$$1 \text{ unit of magnetic field intensity} = 1 \cdot \frac{1 \text{ abampere}}{1 \text{ cm}} = 1\frac{\text{abampere}}{\text{cm}}$$

The unit of magnetic field intensity in the cgs emu system is called the *oersted.*

The oersted (oe) is the magnetic field intensity at a point a distance of 2 cm from an infintely long straight wire, with a negligibly small cross section, carrying a current of 1 abampere.*

The dimensions of the oersted are found from Eq. (5.40):

$$[H] = \frac{[I]}{[r]} = \frac{\text{cm}^{1/2} \cdot \text{g}^{1/2} \cdot \text{sec}^{-1}}{\text{cm}} = \text{cm}^{-1/2} \cdot \text{g}^{1/2} \cdot \text{sec}^{-1}$$

---

*When formulating the cgs emu system by the first method, that is, when using the Coulomb law for the interaction of magnetic poles as the initial fundamental equation, the oersted is defined as follows: the intensity of a uniform magnetic field which acts with a force of 1 dyne on a unit north magnetic pole. The fundamental equation for magnetic field intensity in this case would be:

$$H = \frac{m}{r^2}$$

Magnetic induction (magnetic flux density). The unit of magnetic induction is determined by the equation:

$$B = \mu H \tag{5.41}$$

Since magnetic permeability is a dimensionless quantity in the cgs emu system, it follows from Eq. (5.41) that induction should be measured in the same units as magnetic field strength, that is, in oersteds. However, historically, the unit of magnetic induction came to be known as the gauss. The gauss is the magnetic induction possessed, in a vacuum, by a magnetic field of intensity 1 oersted. The dimensions of the gauss, in accordance with Eq. (5.41), are:

$$[B] = [\mu][H] = cm^{-1/2} \cdot g^{1/2} \cdot sec^{-1}$$

Magnetic induction flux (magnetic flux). The unit of magnetic induction flux is determined from the equation:

$$\Phi = kBS \tag{5.42}$$

where Φ is the magnetic flux passing through an area S (perpendicular to the field) in a uniform magnetic field with induction B.

Assuming, in (5.42), that $k = 1$, B = gauss, and $S = 1$ cm^2, we find:

1 unit of magnetic induction flux = 1 gauss $\cdot$ 1 cm^2 = 1 gauss $\cdot$ cm^2

This unit is called the *maxwell*.

The maxwell is the induction flux passing through 1 cm of area perpendicular to a field with an induction of 1 gauss.

In accordance with (5.42), the dimensions of the maxwell are:

$$[\Phi] = [B][S] = cm^{-1/2} \cdot g^{1/2} \cdot sec^{-1} \cdot cm^2 = cm^{3/2} \cdot g^{1/2} \cdot sec^{-1}$$

Maxwells are also used to measure flux linkage, which is determined by the equation:

$$\Psi = \Phi N$$

where Φ is the magnetic flux passing through the cross section of a solenoid and N is the number of turns in the solenoid.

Magnetic mass (amount of magnetism). The unit of measurement of the magnetic mass m can be derived from the equation:

$$F = kBm$$

from which

$$m = \frac{F}{kB} \tag{5.43}$$

where F is the force with which a magnetic field of induction B acts on a magnetic pole of mass m.

Assuming, in this equation, that $k = 1$, $F = 1$ dyne, and $B = 1$ gauss, we find that:

$$1 \text{ cgs emu } (m) = 1 \cdot \frac{1 \text{ dyne}}{1 \text{ gauss}} = 1 \frac{\text{dyne}}{\text{gauss}}$$

This unit has no particular name.

The unit of magnetic mass in the cgs emu system is taken as the magnetic mass of a pole on which a force of 1 dyne is exerted by a magnetic field of 1 gauss.

The unit of magnetic mass can also be determined from the equation:

$$dF = k \frac{mI \sin \alpha}{r^2} dl$$

which expresses the Biot-Savart law.

We find from this equation that:

$$m = \frac{r^2 dF}{kI \sin \alpha \, dl} \tag{5.44}$$

If we assume that $dl = 1$ cm, $r = 1$ cm, $I = 1$ abampere, $dF = 1$ dyne, $\alpha = \pi/2$ rad, and $k = 1$, then we obtain:

$$1 \text{ cgs emu } (m) = \frac{1 \text{ cm}^2 \cdot 1 \text{ dyne}}{1 \text{ abampere} \cdot 1 \text{ cm}} = 1 \frac{\text{dyne} \cdot \text{cm}}{\text{abampere}}$$

On the basis of Eq. (5.44), the unit of magnetic mass in the cgs emu system can be defined as follows: given a magnetic pole located 1 cm from a wire carrying a current of 1 abampere, the unit of magnetic mass is the magnetic mass at which that pole is acted upon with a force of 1 dyne by a 1-cm segment of the wire.

The dimensions of the unit of magnetic mass can be determined from Eq. (5.43):

$$[m] = \frac{[F]}{[B]} = \frac{\text{cm} \cdot \text{g} \cdot \text{sec}^{-2}}{\text{cm}^{-1/2} \cdot \text{g}^{1/2} \cdot \text{sec}^{-1}} = \text{cm}^{3/2} \cdot \text{g}^{1/2} \cdot \text{sec}^{-1}$$

or from (5.44):

$$[m] = \frac{[r^2][dF]}{[I][dl]} = \frac{\text{cm}^2 \cdot \text{cm} \cdot \text{g} \cdot \text{sec}^{-2}}{\text{cm}^{1/2} \cdot \text{g}^{1/2} \cdot \text{sec} \cdot \text{cm}} = \text{cm}^{3.2} \cdot \text{g}^{1/2} \cdot \text{sec}^{-1}$$

Magnetic moment. The unit of measurement of the magnetic moment can be determined from the formula:

$$M = k \cdot p_m \cdot H \sin \alpha$$

where p_m is the magnetic moment of a magnet or of a loop carrying a current, M is the mechanical moment acting on the magnet (current-carrying loop) in a uniform magnetic field with intensity H, and α is the angle between the direction of the field and the axis of the magnet (normal to the plane of the loop).

From this equation, we obtain:

$$p_m = \frac{1}{k} \frac{M}{H \sin \alpha} \tag{5.45}$$

Assuming, in this formula, that $k = 1$, $H = 1$ oe, $M = 1$ dyne $\cdot$ cm, and $\alpha = 90°$, we find that:

$$1 \text{ cgs emu } (p_m) = 1 \cdot \frac{1 \text{ dyne} \cdot \text{cm}}{1 \text{ oe} \cdot 1} = 1 \frac{\text{dyne} \cdot \text{cm}}{\text{oe}}$$

The unit of magnetic moment in the cgs emu system is taken as the magnetic moment of a permanent straight magnet (or current-carrying loop) on which a maximum torque of 1 dyne $\cdot$ cm acts in a uniform magnetic field.

The unit of magnetic moment can also be determined from the equations:

$$p_m = kml \tag{5.46}$$

where p_m is the magnetic moment of a straight magnet, m is the magnetic mass of the pole of the magnet, and l is the distance between the poles; and:

$$p_m = kIS \tag{5.47}$$

where p_m is the magnetic moment of the current-carrying loop, I is the current in the loop, and S is the area of the loop.

On the basis of Eq. (5.46), we can consider the unit of magnetic moment as the magnetic moment of a straight magnet of length 1 cm, the mass of each of whose poles is equal to 1 cgs emu (m). On the basis of Eq. (5.47), we can consider the unit of magnetic moment as the magnetic moment of a loop with an area of 1 cm^2 and a current of 1 abampere.

All three definitions are formally equivalent.

The dimensions of the unit of magnetic moment can be determined from Eqs. (5.45), (5.46), or (5.47).

From Eq. (5.45), we obtain:

$$[p_m] = \frac{[M]}{[H]} = \frac{\text{cm} \cdot \text{g} \cdot \text{sec}^{-2} \cdot \text{cm}}{\text{cm}^{-1/2} \cdot \text{g}^{1/2} \cdot \text{sec}^{-1}} = \text{cm}^{5/2} \cdot \text{g}^{1/2} \cdot \text{sec}^{-1}$$

We recommend that the reader check for himself that Eqs. (5.46) and (5.47) yield exactly the same dimensions for the magnetic moment.

Amount of electricity (charge). The unit of measurement of the charge q in the cgs emu system is determined from the equation:

$$q = kIt \qquad (5.48)$$

where I is the current in the conductor and t is the time over which this current carries a charge q through the cross section of the conductor.

Assuming, in (5.48), that $k = 1$, $I = 1$ abampere, and $t = 1$ sec, we obtain:

$$1 \text{ cgs emu } (q) = 1 \text{ abampere} \cdot 1 \text{ sec} = 1 \text{ abampere} \cdot \text{sec}$$

The unit of charge in the cgs emu system is called the *abcoulomb*.

It follows that the abcoulomb is taken as the charge carried across the cross section of a conductor in 1 sec by a current equal to 1 abampere.

The dimensions of the abcoulomb are found from Eq. (5.48):

$$[q] = [I][t] = cm^{1/2} \cdot g^{1/2} \cdot sec^{-1} \cdot sec = cm^{1/2} \cdot g^{1/2}$$

Potential (voltage, emf). The unit of potential U in the cgs emu system is determined from the equation:

$$U = k\frac{W}{q} \qquad (5.49)$$

where W is the work done in moving a charge q through a potential difference U.

Assuming, in (5.49), that $k = 1$, $W = 1$ erg, and $q = 1$ abcoulomb, we find that:

$$1 \text{ cgs emu } (U) = 1 \cdot \frac{1 \text{ erg}}{1 \text{ abcoulomb}} = 1\frac{\text{erg}}{\text{abcoulomb}}$$

The unit of potential in the cgs emu system is called the *abvolt*.

It follows that the abvolt is taken as the potential difference for which a work of 1 erg is done by a charge of 1 abcoulomb passing through it.

The dimensions of the abvolt are determined from Eq. (5.49):

$$[U] = \frac{[W]}{[q]} = \frac{cm^2 \cdot g \cdot sec^{-2}}{cm^{1/2} \cdot g^{1/2}} = cm^{3/2} \cdot g^{1/2} \cdot sec^{-2}$$

Inductance (coefficient of self-induction). The unit of inductance is determined from the equation:

$$L = k\frac{\Psi}{I} \qquad (5.50)$$

where Ψ is the magnetic flux of a circuit with inductance L when a current I is passing through it.

Assuming, in (5.50), that $k = 1$, $\Psi = 1$ maxwell and $I = 1$ abampere, we obtain:

$$1 \text{ cgs emu } (L) = 1 \cdot \frac{1 \text{ maxwell}}{1 \text{ abampere}} = 1 \frac{\text{maxwell}}{\text{abampere}}$$

The unit of inductance in the cgs emu system is the *centimeter*.

The centimeter (cm) is the inductance of a circuit in which there is a flux linkage of 1 maxwell at a current of 1 abampere.

The unit of inductance can also be determined from the equation:

$$E_i = -k \frac{d\Psi}{dt} = -kL \frac{dI}{dt}$$

expressing the Faraday-Maxwell law for emf of self-induction.

From this formula, we can find that:

$$L = -\frac{1}{k} \frac{E_i}{\frac{dI}{dt}} \tag{5.51}$$

where E_i is the emf of self-induction occurring in a circuit when the current varies by dI/dt per unit of time, and L is the inductance of the circuit.

Assuming, in (5.51), that $k = 1$, $E_i = 1$ abvolt, and $dI/dt = 1$ abampere/sec, we obtain:

$$1 \text{ cm} = 1 \cdot \frac{1 \text{ abvolt}}{1 \dfrac{\text{abampere}}{\text{sec}}} = 1 \frac{\text{abvolt} \cdot \text{sec}}{\text{abampere}}$$

On the basis of Eq. (5.51), the centimeter is defined as follows: the inductance of a circuit in which there is a self-induced emf of 1 abvolt when the current in the circuit varies 1 abampere in one second.

We find from Eqs. (5.50) and (5.51) that the unit of inductance in the cgs emu system has the dimension cm.

Since electrostatic quantities, with very rare exceptions, are not measured in cgs emu units, we will not derive them from the fundamental equations. If necessary, the reader can do this for himself by using the fundamental equations in Table 9.

4. THE CGS SYSTEM (GAUSSIAN SYSTEM)

The fundamental units in the cgs system (Gaussian) are the same as in the cgs esu and cgs emu systems, that is:

The centimeter (cm)—the unit of length;

The gram (g)—the unit of mass;

The second (sec)—the unit time.

The derived units in the cgs system (Gaussian) have been selected in the following way: as units for measuring electric quantities the units of the cgs esu system are used; while for measuring magnetic quantities, cgs emu units are used.

In the formulation of the cgs (Gaussian) system, the dielectric permittivity and the magnetic permeability of a vacuum are both taken as equal to unity and as dimensionless quantities. This arbitrary assignment of numerical values and dimensions to both the dielectric permittivity and the magnetic permeability means that we can no longer assume that the proportionality factor k contained in the electromagnetic equations is equal to unity. Hence, in order to satisfy the relationships between physical quantities we must, when formulating the cgs (Gaussian) system, determine the correct proportionality constants in electromagnetic formulas containing both electric and magnetic quantities. In some formulas, this constant is found to be $1/c$, and in others, $1/c^2$ (where c is the electrodynamic constant, equal numerically and in dimension to the speed of light, that is, $c \approx 3 \cdot 10^{10}$ cm/sec).

Let us consider some equations for electromagnetic quantities in the cgs (Gaussian) system.

The magnetic field intensity created by an infinitely long straight current is:

$$H = \frac{1}{c} \frac{2I}{r}$$

The magnetic field intensity at the center of a circular current is:

$$H = \frac{1}{c} \frac{2\pi I}{r}$$

The force acting on an element of a wire of length 1 m when two infinitely long, parallel current-carrying wires interact is:

$$F = \frac{1}{c^2} \frac{2I_1 \cdot I_2}{r} l$$

The force acting on a charge moving in a magnetic field (Lorentz force) is:

$$F = \frac{1}{c} evH \sin \alpha$$

The magnetic moment of a current-carrying circuit in a vacuum is:

$$p_m = \frac{1}{c} ISN$$

The work necessary to move a current-carrying circuit in a magnetic field is:

$$W = \frac{1}{c} I(\Phi_2 - \Phi_1)$$

The induced electromotive force (Faraday's law) is:

$$E = -\frac{1}{c} \frac{d\Psi}{dt}$$

The self-induced electromotive force is:

$$E = -\frac{1}{c^2} L \frac{dI}{dt}$$

The flux linkage of a solenoid is:

$$\Psi = \frac{1}{c} LI$$

5. THE RATIONALIZED MKSAR SYSTEM

Many equations describing electric and magnetic phenomena contain the factor 4π. This factor is found in the formulas most commonly encountered in practice, for example:
capacitance of a plane condenser:

$$C = \frac{\varepsilon S}{4\pi d}$$

magnetic field strength of a circular current:

$$H = \frac{2\pi I}{r}$$

magnetic field strength of a solenoid:

$$H = 4\pi In$$

magnetomotive force:

$$E_m = 4\pi IN$$

etc.

Table 10

Unrationalized and Rationalized Forms of the Most Common Electromagnetic Equations*

Physical quantity	Equation	
	Unrationalized	Rationalized
Force of interaction between point sources (Coulomb's law)	$F = \dfrac{q_1 \cdot q_2}{\epsilon r^2}$	$F = \dfrac{q_1 \cdot q_2}{4\pi\epsilon r^2}$
Field intensity of point charge	$E = \dfrac{q}{\epsilon \cdot r^2}$	$E = \dfrac{q}{4\pi\epsilon \cdot r^2}$
Induced flux of electric charges (based on Ostrogradskiy–Gauss theorem)	$N = \dfrac{4\pi}{\epsilon}\Sigma q$	$N = \dfrac{\Sigma q}{\epsilon}$
Field intensity of charged segment of line	$E = \dfrac{2\eta}{\epsilon \cdot r}$	$E = \dfrac{\eta}{2\pi\epsilon \cdot r}$
Field intensity of charged sphere	$E = \dfrac{q}{\epsilon \cdot r^2}$	$E = \dfrac{q}{4\pi\epsilon \cdot r^2}$
Field intensity of charged plane	$E = \dfrac{2\pi\sigma}{\epsilon}$	$E = \dfrac{\sigma}{2\epsilon}$
Field intensity of plane condenser	$E = \dfrac{4\pi\sigma}{\epsilon}$	$E = \dfrac{\sigma}{\epsilon}$
Field potential of point charge	$U = \dfrac{q}{\epsilon \cdot r}$	$U = \dfrac{q}{4\pi\epsilon \cdot r}$
Capacitance of plane condenser	$C = \dfrac{\epsilon S}{4\pi \cdot d}$	$C = \dfrac{\epsilon S}{d}$
Capacitance of sphere	$C = \epsilon \cdot r$	$C = 4\pi\epsilon \cdot r$

Force of interaction between plane condenser plates	$F = \dfrac{\epsilon S U^2}{8\pi \cdot d^2}$	$F = \dfrac{\epsilon S U^2}{2d^2}$
Energy of plane condenser	$W = \dfrac{\epsilon S U^2}{8\pi \cdot d}$	$W = \dfrac{\epsilon S U^2}{2d}$
Magnetic field intensity of a current (Biot–Savart law)	$dH = \dfrac{I \sin\alpha\, dl}{r^2}$	$dH = \dfrac{I \sin\alpha\, dl}{4\pi \cdot r^2}$
Magnetic field intensity of a straight current	$H = \dfrac{2I}{r}$	$H = \dfrac{I}{2\pi \cdot r}$
Magnetic field intensity of a circular current	$H = \dfrac{2\pi I}{r}$	$H = \dfrac{I}{2r}$
Magnetic field intensity of a solenoid	$H = 4\pi I n$	$H = I \cdot n$
Force of interaction of parallel currents	$F = \dfrac{2\mu I_1 I_2 l}{r}$	$F = \dfrac{\mu I_1 I_2 l}{2\pi r}$
Magnetic field energy density	$\omega = \dfrac{\mu H^2}{8\pi}$	$\omega = \dfrac{\mu H^2}{2}$
Magnetic flux in linear circuit (Hopkinson's formula)	$\Phi = \dfrac{4\pi I n}{\dfrac{l}{\mu S} + \dfrac{l_0}{\mu_0 S_0}}$	$\Phi = \dfrac{I n}{\dfrac{l}{\mu S} + \dfrac{l_0}{\mu_0 S_0}}$
Magnetic moment of current-carrying circuit	$p_m = \mu I S$	$p_m = \dfrac{\mu I S}{4\pi}$
Inductance (coefficient of self-induction of a solenoid)	$L = 4\pi \mu n^2 V$	$L = \mu n^2 V$

*Equations which are the same in both the rationalized and unrationalized forms are not given in this table.

The following amplification was first pointed out by O. Heaviside. The factor 4π can be placed in the denominator of the equation expressing Coulomb's law for the interaction of electric charges (that is, we write Coulomb's law in the form $F = \frac{q_1 q_2}{4\pi\varepsilon r^2}$), and can also be placed in the denominator of the equation expressing Coulomb's law for the interaction of magnetic poles (that is, $F = \frac{m_1 m_2}{4\pi\mu r^2}$). Then (after the other electromagnetic equations are modified aqcordingly), the factor 4π disappears from all the other formulas commonly used. This considerably simplifies calculations made using these formulas.

If the formulation of the system of units for electromagnetic quantities is based on the law of interaction of currents, then, in order to simplify the equations commonly encountered in practice, the multiplier 4π should be placed in the denominator of the formula for Ampere's law.

When transformed in this way, the electromagnetic formulas are said to be rationalized, and the system of units for which this transformation is made is called a rationalized system.

Any system can be rationalized, but, in fact, only the rationalized MKSAr system is in use. Simplification of the theoretical formulas in this system is of practical interest.

The rationalized MKSA system is denoted by MKSAr. The system is widely employed in electrical and electronics engineering.

The rationalized equations can be obtained from the unrationalized equations in the following manner:

a) in equations containing the dielectric permittivity ε, the electric field induction D, or the magnetic field intensity H, multiply the symbol ε, D, or H (as the case may be) by the factor 4π.

b) in equations containing the magnetic permeability μ, multiply μ by $1/4\pi$.

Electromagnetic equations which do not contain ε, D, H, or μ have the same form in both the rationalized and unrationalized systems.

Electromagnetic formulas for the rationalized and unrationalized systems are compared in Table 10.

6. RELATIONSHIPS AMONG ELECTROMAGNETIC UNITS IN DIFFERENT SYSTEMS

The relationships among electromagnetic units in different systems are shown in Table 11. This table makes possible the direct expression of MKSA units in terms of units of the other systems. It would also be possible to compile similar tables for the other systems, but there is no need to do so. Table 11 enables us to find the relationship between the units of any pair of systems.

Table 11

Relations Among Units in MKSA System and Units in Other Systems

Name of quantity	Symbol	Designated unit in MKSA system	Corresponding equivalent for the unit in the MKSA system		
			cgs esu	cgs emu	MKSAr
Current	I	1 amp	$3 \cdot 10^9$	10^{-1}	1
Charge	q	1 coulomb	$3 \cdot 10^9$	10^{-1}	1
Surface charge density	σ	$1\dfrac{\text{coulomb}}{\text{m}^2}$	$3 \cdot 10^5$	10^{-5}	1
Potential	U	1 volt	$\dfrac{1}{300}$	10^8	1
Capacitance	C	1 farad	$9 \cdot 10^{11}$	10^{-9}	1
Resistance	R	1 ohm	$\dfrac{1}{9} 10^{-11}$	10^9	1
Dielectric permittivity	ϵ	1 f/m	$9 \cdot 10^9$	10^{-11}	$\dfrac{1}{4\pi}$
Electric field intensity	E	1 v/m	$\dfrac{1}{3} 10^{-4}$	10^6	1
Electric induction (displacement)	D	$1\dfrac{\text{coulomb}}{\text{m}^2}$	$3 \cdot 10^5$	10^{-5}	$\dfrac{1}{4\pi}$
Electric induction flux	N	1 coulomb	$3 \cdot 10^9$	10^{-1}	$\dfrac{1}{4\pi}$
Magnetic induction flux	Φ	1 weber	$\dfrac{1}{300}$	10^8	1
Magnetic induction	B	$1\dfrac{\text{weber}}{\text{m}^2}$	$\dfrac{1}{3} 10^{-6}$	10^4	1
Magnetic field intensity	H	$1\dfrac{\text{amp}}{\text{m}}$	$3 \cdot 10^7$	10^{-3}	$\dfrac{1}{4\pi}$
Magnetic permeability	μ	$1\dfrac{\text{henry}}{\text{m}}$	$\dfrac{1}{9} 10^{-13}$	10^7	4π
Magnetomagnetic force	E_m	1 amp	$3 \cdot 10^9$	10^{-1}	$\dfrac{1}{4\pi}$
Magnetic moment	p_m	1 weber × m	$\dfrac{1}{3}$	10^{10}	4π
Inductance	L	1 henry	$\dfrac{1}{9} 10^{-11}$	10^9	1

For example, suppose that we wish to express the unit of magnetic field intensity of the cgs emu system in terms of cgs esu units. To do this, we form an equation from the table:

$$3 \cdot 10^7 \text{cgs esu } (H) = 10^{-3} \text{cgs emu } (H)$$

and find that:

$$1 \text{ cgs emu } (H) = \frac{3 \cdot 10^7 \text{ cgs esu } (H)}{10^{-3}} = 3 \cdot 10^{10} \text{ cgs esu } (H)$$

Thus:

$$1 \text{ cgs emu } (H) = 3 \cdot 10^{10} \text{ cgs esu } (H)$$

In order to see how the relationships given in Table 11 have been derived, let us make the relevant calculations for some electromagnetic quantities.

Current. a) The relationship between the absolute electromagnetic unit of current (the abampere) and the unit of current in the cgs esu system (the statampere) was established experimentally.

In view of the great importance of this relationship, let us consider the method by which it was established.

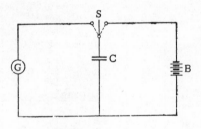

Fig. 1

If the condenser C (see Fig. 1) is charged (from battery B using the switch S) and discharged (through a tangent-galvanometer) many times per second, then the current flowing through the galvanometer G can be expressed in electrostatic as well as in electromagnetic units. Each time the condenser is discharged through the galvanometer, there is an electric charge:

$$q = CU$$

where C is the capacitance of the condenser and U is the potential to which the condenser is charged by the battery.

If the condenser has been charged and discharged n' times over a period t, the total charge which has passed through the galvanometer is:

$$Q = n'q = n'CU$$

while the mean current in electrostatic units is:

$$I_e = \frac{Q}{t} = \frac{n'CU}{t} = nCU \tag{5.52}$$

where $n = n'/t$ is the number of times the condenser has been charged and discharged per sec.

Let α be the angle of deflection of the tangent galvanometer needle when the current passes through it (Fig. 2). If the plane of the coils in the galvanometer lies in the plane of the magnetic meridian, the angle α satisfies the equation:

$$\tan \alpha = \frac{H_T}{H_0} \tag{5.53}$$

where H_T is the magnetic field intensity created by the current and H_0 is the horizontal component of the earth's magnetic field.

But:

$$H_T = \frac{2\pi I_m N}{r} \tag{5.54}$$

where I_m is the current expressed in electromagnetic units, N is the number of coils in the tangent galvonometer, and r is the radius of the coils.

Fig. 2

Substituting H_T into Eq. (5.53), and expressing it in terms of I_m, we obtain:

$$I_m = \frac{H_0 r \tan \alpha}{2\pi N} \tag{5.55}$$

Dividing (5.52) by (5.55), we find the ratio c of the current expressed in electrostatic units and the current expressed in electromagnetic units:

$$c = \frac{I_e}{I_m} = \frac{2\pi NnCU}{H_0 r \tan i}$$

Precise experiments have shown that this ratio is numerically equal to the speed of light. Let us ascertain the dimensions of this ratio.

Tables 8 and 9 show us that:

$$[I_e] = cm^{3/2} \cdot g^{1/2} \cdot sec^{-2}$$

$$[I_m] = cm^{1/2} \cdot g^{1/2} \cdot sec^{-1}$$

from which

$$[c] = \frac{[I_e]}{[I_m]} = \frac{cm^{3/2} \cdot g^{1/2} \cdot sec^{-2}}{cm^{1/2} \cdot g^{1/2} \cdot sec^{-1}} = cm \cdot sec^{-1}$$

Thus, the ratio of the current expressed in cgs esu (I) units to the current expressed in cgs emu (I) units, both numerically and in terms of dimensions, is equal to the speed of the light $c \approx 3 \cdot 10^{10}$ cm/sec.

It follows from this that the unit of current cgs emu (I) (the abampere) is greater than the unit of current cgs esu (I) (the stat-ampere) by a factor of c, that is:

$$1 \text{ abampere} = 3 \cdot 10^{10} \text{ statamperes} \tag{5.56}$$

The quantity c, which expresses the ratio between the electro-magnetic unit of current and the electrostatic unit, is called the *electrodynamic constant.*

b) The relationship between the ampere and the abampere is known from the definition of the ampere. The ampere, as the funda-mental unit in the MKSA system, has been arbitrarily selected as equal to one tenth of an abampere, that is:

$$1 \text{ amp} = 0.1 \text{ abampere} \tag{5.57}$$

By comparing Eqs. (5.56) and (5.57), we find the relationship be-tween the units of current, as shown in Table 11:

$$1 \text{ amp} = 3 \cdot 10^9 \text{ cgs esu } (I) = 0.1 \text{ cgs emu } (I)$$

Magnetic field intensity. The relationship between the units of magnetic field intensity can be derived from the formula for the magnetic field intensity exerted by an infinitely long, straight con-ductor (wire) carrying a current:

$$H = \frac{2I}{r}$$

This formula gives us three equations determining the unit of magnetic field intensity in the different systems:

in the cgs emu system:

$$1 \text{ oe} = \frac{2 \cdot 1 \text{ abampere}}{2 \text{ cm}} = \frac{1 \text{ abampere}}{1 \text{ cm}} \qquad (5.58)$$

in the cgs esu system:

$$1 \text{ statoersted} = \frac{2 \cdot 1 \text{ statampere}}{2 \text{ cm}} = \frac{1 \text{ statampere}}{1 \text{ cm}} \qquad (5.59)$$

in the MKSA system:

$$1 \frac{\text{ampere}}{\text{meter}} = \frac{2 \cdot 1 \text{ amp}}{2 \text{ m}} = \frac{1 \text{ amp}}{1 \text{ meter}} \qquad (5.60)$$

Dividing (5.58) by (5.59), we obtain:

$$\frac{1 \text{ oe}}{1 \text{ statoersted}} = \frac{1 \text{ abampere} \cdot 1 \text{ cm}}{1 \text{ cm} \cdot 1 \text{ statampere}} = \frac{3 \cdot 10^{10} \text{ statampere}}{1 \text{ statampere}} = 3 \cdot 10^{10}$$

or:

$$1 \text{ oe} = 3 \cdot 10^{10} \text{ statoersteds} \qquad (5.61)$$

Dividing (5.60) by (5.58), we obtain:

$$\frac{1 \frac{\text{amp}}{\text{m}}}{1 \text{ oe}} = \frac{1 \text{ amp} \cdot 1 \text{ cm}}{1 \text{ m} \cdot 1 \text{ abampere}} = \frac{0.1 \text{ abampere} \cdot 1 \text{ cm}}{100 \text{ cm} \cdot 1 \text{ abampere}} = 10^{-3}$$

or:

$$1 \frac{\text{amp}}{\text{m}} = 10^{-3} \text{ oe} \qquad (5.62)$$

From equations (5.61) and (5.62) we obtain:

$$1 \frac{\text{amp}}{\text{m}} = 10^{-3} \text{ oe} = 3 \cdot 10^{7} \text{ statoersteds}$$

that is, we arrive at the relationship found in Table 11.

Magnetic permeability. The relationships among the units of magnetic permeability can be established using Ampere's law:

$$F = \frac{2 \mu I_1 I_2}{r} l$$

from which:

$$\mu = \frac{Fr}{2l_1 l_2 l}$$

This equation gives us three equalities determining the units of magnetic permeability in different systems:

in the cgs emu system:

$$1 \text{ cgs emu } (\mu) = \frac{1 \text{ dyne} \cdot 2 \text{ cm}}{2 (1 \text{ abampere})^2 \cdot 1 \text{ cm}} = \frac{1 \text{ dyne}}{(1 \text{ abampere})^2} \tag{5.63}$$

in the cgs esu system:

$$1 \text{ cgs esu } (\mu) = \frac{1 \text{ dyne} \cdot 2 \text{ cm}}{2 (1 \text{ statampere})^2 \cdot 1 \text{ cm}} = \frac{1 \text{ dyne}}{(1 \text{ statampere})^2} \tag{5.64}$$

in the MKSA system:

$$1 \text{ MKSA } (\mu) = \frac{1 \text{ N} \cdot 2 \text{ m}}{2 (1 \text{ amp})^2 \cdot 1 \text{ m}} = \frac{1 \text{ N}}{(1 \text{ amp})^2} \tag{5.65}$$

Dividing (5.63) by (5.64), we find that:

$$\frac{1 \text{ cgs emu } (\mu)}{1 \text{ cgs esu } (\mu)} = \frac{1 \text{ dyne} \cdot (1 \text{ statampere})^2}{(1 \text{ abampere})^2 \cdot 1 \text{ dyne}}$$

$$= \frac{(1 \text{ statampere})^2}{9 \cdot 10^{20} (1 \text{ statampere})^2} = \frac{1}{9} \cdot 10^{-20}$$

or:

$$1 \text{ cgs emu } (\mu) = \frac{1}{9} \cdot 10^{-20} \text{ cgs esu } (\mu) \tag{5.66}$$

Dividing (5.65) by (5.63), we obtain:

$$\frac{1 \text{ MKSA } (\mu)}{1 \text{ cgs emu } (\mu)} = \frac{1 \text{ N} \cdot (1 \text{ abampere})^2}{(1 \text{ amp})^2 \cdot 1 \text{ dyne}}$$

$$= \frac{10^5 \text{ dyne } (1 \text{ abampere})^2}{10^{-2} (1 \text{ abampere})^2 \cdot 1 \text{ dyne}} = 10^7$$

from which:

$$1 \text{ MKSA } (\mu) = 10^7 \text{ cgs emu } (\mu)$$

or:

$$1 \frac{h}{m} = 10^7 \text{ cgs emu } (\mu) \tag{5.67}$$

Comparing equations (5.66) and (5.67), we obtain the relationship found in Table 11, that is:

$$1\,\frac{h}{m} = \frac{1}{9} \cdot 10^{-13} \text{ cgs esu } (\mu) = 10^7 \text{ cgs emu } (\mu)$$

In exactly the same way, using the formulas for the dependence between electromagnetic quantities, we can derive the other relationships shown in Table 11.

7. SAMPLE SOLUTIONS OF PROBLEMS IN ELECTROMAGNETISM

Example 1. Calculate the force of interaction between two point charges $q_1 = 0.3 \cdot 10^{-6}$ coulomb and $q_2 = 4000$ statcoulombs 10 cm apart in paraffin.

Solution. The force of interaction between electric charges is determined from Coulomb's law:

$$F = \frac{q_1 \cdot q_2}{\varepsilon \cdot r^2} \tag{1}$$

Calculation in the cgs esu system:

$q_1 = 0.3 \cdot 10^{-6}$ coulomb $= 0.3 \cdot 10^{-6} \cdot 3 \cdot 10^9 = 0.9 \cdot 10^3$ statcoulomb
$q_2 = 4000$ statcoulomb $= 4 \cdot 10^3$ statcoulomb
$r = 10$ cm

In order to calculate ε, we must know the relative value of the dielectric permittivity of paraffin and the value of ε_0 in the cgs esu system:

$$\left.\begin{array}{l} \varepsilon_r = 2 \\ \varepsilon_0 = 1 \end{array}\right\} \quad \varepsilon = \varepsilon_r \cdot \varepsilon_0 = 2 \cdot 1 = 2$$

Substituting the numerical values into Eq. (1), we obtain:

$$F = \frac{0.9 \cdot 10^3 \cdot 4 \cdot 10^3}{2 \cdot 10^2} = 1.8 \cdot 10^4 \text{ dyne}$$

Calculation in the cgs emu system:

$q_1 = 0.3 \cdot 10^{-6}$ coulomb $= 0.3 \cdot 10^{-6} \cdot 10^{-1} = 0.3 \cdot 10^{-7}$ abcoulomb
$q_2 = 4000$ statcoulomb $= 4 \cdot 10^3 \cdot \dfrac{1}{3 \cdot 10^{10}} = \dfrac{4}{3} \cdot 10^{-7}$ abcoulomb
$r = 10$ cm
$\varepsilon_r = 2$; $\varepsilon_0 = 1.1 \cdot 10^{-21}$ cm$^{-2} \cdot$ sec^2
$\varepsilon = \varepsilon_r \cdot \varepsilon_0 = 2 \cdot 1.1 \cdot 10^{-21}$ cm$^{-2} \cdot$ sec$^2 = 2.2 \cdot 10^{-21}$ cm$^{-2} \cdot$ sec^2

Substituting numerical values into Eq. (1), we obtain:

$$F = \frac{0.3 \cdot 10^{-7} \cdot \frac{4}{3} \cdot 10^{-7}}{2.2 \cdot 10^{-21} \cdot 10^{2}} = 1.8 \cdot 10^{4} \text{ dyne}$$

Calculation in the MKSA system:

$q_1 = 0.3 \cdot 10^{-6}$ coulomb

$q_2 = 4000$ statcoulomb $= 4 \cdot 10^3 \cdot \frac{1}{3} \cdot 10^{-9} = \frac{4}{3} \cdot 10^{-6}$ coulomb

$r = 10$ cm $= 0.1$ m

$\varepsilon_r = 2$

$\varepsilon_0 = 1.1 \cdot 10^{-10} \frac{f}{m}$ $\Big\}$ $\varepsilon = \varepsilon_r \cdot \varepsilon_0 = 2 \cdot 1.1 \cdot 10^{-10} \frac{f}{m} 2.2 \cdot 10^{-10} \frac{f}{m}$

After substitution of the numerical values, we obtain:

$$F = \frac{0.3 \cdot 10^{-6} \cdot \frac{4}{3} \cdot 10^{-6}}{2.2 \cdot 10^{-10} \cdot (0.1)^2} = 0.18 \text{ N}$$

Calculation in the MKSAr system:
In this system Coulomb's law takes the form (see Table 10):

$$F = \frac{q_1 \cdot q_2}{4\pi\varepsilon r^2} \tag{2}$$

Let us write the values of all quantities contained in the data given for the problem, and let us express them in the MKSAr system:

$q_1 = 0.3 \cdot 10^{-6}$ coulomb

$q_2 = 4000$ statcoulomb $= 4 \cdot 10^3 \cdot \frac{1}{3} \cdot 10^{-9} = \frac{4}{3} \cdot 10^{-6}$ coulomb

$r = 10$ cm $= 0.1$ m

$\varepsilon_r = 2$

$\varepsilon_0 = 8.8 \cdot 10^{-12} \frac{f}{m}$ $\Big\}$ $\varepsilon = \varepsilon_r \cdot \varepsilon_0 = 2 \cdot 8.8 \cdot 10^{-12} = 1.8 \cdot 10^{-11} \frac{f}{m}$

Substituting numerical values into Eq. (2), we obtain:

$$F = \frac{0.3 \cdot 10^{-6} \cdot \frac{4}{3} \cdot 10^{-6}}{4 \cdot 3.14 \cdot 1.8 \cdot 10^{-11} \cdot (0.1)^2} = 0.18 \text{ N}$$

Example 2. A solenoid without a core has 10 turns per centimeter and an inductance of 0.01 h. What is the length of the solenoid if its diameter is 20 cm?

Solution. The inductance of the solenoid is expressed by the equation:

$$L = 4\pi\mu n^2 V = 4\pi\mu n^2 l \cdot S$$

where n is the number of turns per unit length, V is the volume of the solenoid, l is its length, and S is its cross-sectional area.

This gives us the length of the solenoid:

$$l = \frac{L}{4\pi\mu n^2 S}$$

Calculation in the cgs emu system:
Let us write the quantities in the cgs emu system:

$$n = 10 \text{ cm}^{-1}$$
$$L = 0.01 \text{ h} = 0.01 \cdot 10^9 = 10^7 \text{ cm}$$
$$S = \pi R^2 = \pi \cdot 10^2 = 100\,\pi \text{ cm}^2$$
$$\left.\begin{array}{l} \mu_r = 1 \\ \mu_0 = 1 \end{array}\right\} \quad \mu = \mu_r \cdot \mu_0 = 1 \cdot 1 = 1$$

Substituting numerical values into the equation for the length of the solenoid, we obtain:

$$l = \frac{10^7}{4\,\pi \cdot 1 \cdot 10^2 \cdot 100\,\pi} = 25 \text{ cm}$$

Calculation in the MKSA system:
Let us write the quantities in the MKSA system:

$$n = 10 \text{ cm}^{-1} = 10^3 \text{ m}^{-1}$$
$$L = 0.01 \text{ h}$$
$$S = \pi \cdot (10\,\text{cm})^2 = \pi\,(0.1 \text{ m})^2 = 0.01 \cdot \pi \text{ m}^2$$
$$\left.\begin{array}{l} \mu_r = 1 \\ \mu_0 = 10^{-7}\dfrac{\text{h}}{\text{m}} \end{array}\right\} \quad \mu = \mu_r \cdot \mu_0 = 1 \cdot 10^{-7}\dfrac{\text{h}}{\text{m}} = 10^{-7}\dfrac{\text{h}}{\text{m}}$$

Substituting numerical values into the equation for the length of the solenoid, we find that:

$$l = \frac{0.01}{4\pi \cdot 10^{-7} \cdot (10^3)^2 \cdot 0.01\pi} = 0.25 \text{ m}$$

Calculation in the MKSAr system:
The formula for the inductance of the solenoid in the MKSAr system takes the form:

$$L = \mu n^2 V = \mu n^2 \cdot lS$$

Thus, the length of the solenoid is:

$$l = \frac{L}{\mu n^2 S}$$

Let us write the quantities in the MKSAr system:

$n = 10 \text{ cm}^{-1} = 10^3 \text{ m}^{-1}$
$L = 0.01 \text{ h}$
$S = \pi (10 \text{ cm})^2 = \pi (0.1 \text{ m})^2 = 0.01 \, \pi \, \text{m}^2$
$\mu_r = 1$
$\mu_0 = 4\pi \cdot 10^{-7} \, \dfrac{h}{m}$ $\left.\right\}$ $\mu = \mu_r \cdot \mu_0 = 1 \cdot 4\pi \cdot 10^{-7} = 4\pi \cdot 10^{-7} \, \dfrac{h}{m}$

Substituting numerical values into the equation for the length of the solenoid, we obtain:

$$l = \frac{0.01}{4\pi \cdot 10^{-7} \cdot (10^3)^2 \cdot 0.01\,\pi} = 0.25 \text{ m}$$

Chapter VI

UNITS OF MEASUREMENT OF QUANTITIES OF ELECTROMAGNETIC RADIATION

Electromagnetic waves are characterized by wavelength and method of excitation. The range of electromagnetic waves which have been subjected to scientific study begins with radiowaves, of wavelength 10^6 cm, and extends to x-rays, with a wavelength of 10^{-12} cm. The methods of producing electromagnetic radiation are also varied. Among the sources of electromagnetic waves are the standard electric vibrator, the tube generator, atoms and molecules (when they experience oscillations of the electric charges within them), atomic nuclei undergoing radioactive decay, etc.

Although they may differ in wavelength and mode of excitation, most types of electromagnetic radiation have certain properties in common and can be described by common physical quantities. Such properties are volumetric density of the energy, energy flux, intensity of energy flux, and surface density of energy flux.

There are also units of measurement, common to all types of electromagnetic waves, which are used to measure the general physical quantities describing electromagnetic radiation.

In addition, however, electromagnetic waves possess certain properties which are dependent on wavelength. For example, light waves (waves ranging in wavelength from 0.4 to 0.76 μ) are capable of producing a sensation in human beings. Electromagnetic waves in the range 10^{-2} cm to 0.76 μ exhibit thermal properties to a greater extent than do other waves. X-rays, with wavelengths from 120 to 0.06 Å,* and also gamma rays, which have even shorter wavelengths, possess great penetrating power.** So as to give a quantitative description of the properties of the different kinds of rays, we will have to introduce various quantities and units.

This chapter deals with units of measurements of quantities characterizing electromagnetic radiation.

---

*The angstrom (Å) is a unit of length equal to 10^{-8} cm.
**It should be stressed that there is no sharp borderline between the two types of rays, since the upper boundaries of the one type and the lower boundaries of the other overlap. For example, the range 0.2 Å to 0.06 Å covers both x-rays and gamma rays. Hence, rays are principally distinguished according to the method by which they are produced.

1. UNITS OF MEASUREMENT OF ENERGY QUANTITIES IN ELECTROMAGNETIC RADIATION

Energy density of electromagnetic radiation. The *energy density* is the amount of energy contained in a unit volume.

There are two radiation energy densities:

1. *Integral energy density*, that is, the total energy of the electromagnetic radiation for all wavelengths present in the unit volume.

The integral energy density w is determined from the equation:

$$w = \frac{dW}{dV} \tag{6.1}$$

where dW is the total energy for all wavelengths present in the volume dV.

It follows from this equation that the unit of measurement of the integral energy density is:

in the MKS system, J/m^3; and

in the cgs system, erg/cm^3.

Substituting the dimensions of energy and volume into Eq. (6.1), we find the dimensions of the unit of integral radiation energy density.

In the MKS system:

$$[w] = \frac{[W]}{[V]} = \frac{m^2 \cdot kg \cdot sec^{-2}}{m^3} = m^{-1} \cdot kg \cdot sec^{-2}$$

In the cgs system:

$$[w] = \frac{[W]}{[V]} = \frac{cm^2 \cdot g \cdot sec^{-2}}{cm^3} = cm^{-1} \cdot g \cdot sec^{-2}$$

2. *Spectral energy density.* Let us isolate the electromagnetic radiation with wavelength from λ to $\lambda_1 = \lambda + d\lambda$, and determine the radiation energy, in a unit volume of wavelengths within the range $d\lambda$. The ratio:

$$w_\lambda = \frac{dw}{d\lambda} \tag{6.2}$$

is called the *spectral radiation energy density*. It follows from (6.2) that the spectral energy density is a quantity numerically equal to the energy concentrated in a unit volume and corresponding to a single interval of wavelengths near the wavelength λ.

From this equation, we find that the spectral energy density is measured:

in the MKS system, in $J/(m^3 \cdot m)$, with dimensions $m^{-2} \cdot kg \cdot sec^{-2}$;

in the cgs system, in erg/(cm³ · cm), with dimensions cm⁻² · g · sec⁻².

These units are used to measure the spectral energy density over the radio waveband. For electromagnetic waves of shorter wavelength, including the visible spectrum, we use the units J/(m³ · Å) and erg/(cm³ · Å), since the lengths of these waves are usually measured in Angstrom units.

The spectral density can also be determined with respect to the frequency interval. In this case, the spectral energy density of radiation w_ν is taken as the energy concentrated in a unit volume and corresponding to a single interval of frequencies close to the frequency ν.

The units of measurement of spectral density, referred to the unit frequency interval, can be determined from the equation:

$$w_\nu = \frac{dw}{d\nu} \tag{6.3}$$

It follows from this equation that the spectral energy density is measured:

in the MKS system, in J/(m³ · sec⁻¹), with dimensions m⁻¹ · kg · sec⁻¹;

in the cgs system, in erg/(cm³ · sec⁻¹), with dimensions cm⁻¹ · g · sec⁻¹.

Radiant energy flux (radiant flux). The energy flux of electromagnetic radiation over a surface is the energy transferred by electromagnetic waves through a given surface per unit time.

The following kinds of energy flux are usually considered:

1. The *integral radiant flux* Φ, that is, the total energy transferred through an area S by waves of all wavelengths per unit time. The integral flux is determined from the equation:

$$\Phi = \frac{dW}{dt} \tag{6.4}$$

where dW is the energy transferred over the surface in the time dt.

It follows from (6.4) that the integral flux is measured in units of power, that is:

in the MKS system, in J/sec (watt); and

in the cgs system, in erg/sec.

2. *Spectral radiant energy flux.* This flux $\Phi_\lambda (\Phi_\nu)$ is the energy transferred by electromagnetic waves through an area S per unit time and per unit interval of wavelength near a wavelength λ (or per unit interval of frequency near a frequency ν).

The spectral energy flux is determined from the equations:

$$\Phi_\lambda = \frac{d\Phi}{d\lambda} \tag{6.5}$$

$$\Phi_\nu = \frac{d\Phi}{d\nu} \tag{6.6}$$

It follows from these equations that the spectral energy flux is measured:

in the MKS system, in watts/m, with dimensions $m \cdot kg \cdot sec^{-3}$, or in watts/sec^{-1} with dimensions $m^2 \cdot kg \cdot sec^{-2}$;

in the cgs system, in erg/(sec · cm), with dimensions $cm \cdot g \cdot sec^{-3}$, or in erg/(sec · sec^{-1}), with dimensions $cm^2 \cdot g \cdot sec^{-2}$.

These units are used to measure the spectral radiant energy flux for electromagnetic wavelengths. In the region of shorter wavelengths, we use the units watts/Å and erg/(sec · Å).

Energy flux intensity. The surface energy flux density or energy flux intensity is the energy flux through a unit of surface.

There are two energy flux intensities:

1. *The integral energy flux intensity.* The integral energy flux intensity is the total flux through a unit of surface.

The integral flux intensity *I* is determined from the equation:

$$I = \frac{d\Phi}{dS} \tag{6.7}$$

where $d\Phi$ is the integral energy flux through the surface dS.

It follows from (6.7) that the integral flux intensity is measured:

in the MKS system, in watt/m^2, with dimensions of $kg \cdot sec^{-3}$, and

in the cgs system, in erg/(sec · cm^2), with dimensions of $g \cdot sec^{-5}$.

2. The *spectral energy flux intensity.* The spectral radiant energy flux intensity $I_\lambda(I_\nu)$ is the spectral energy flux passing through a unit area.

The spectral flux intensity is determined by the equations:

$$I_\lambda = \frac{d\Phi_\lambda}{dS} \tag{6.8}$$

$$I_\nu = \frac{d\Phi_\nu}{dS} \tag{6.9}$$

where $d\Phi_\lambda(d\Phi_\nu)$ is the spectral energy flux through an area dS.

It follows from these equations that the spectral flux intensity is measured:

in the MKS system, in watt/(m · m^2), with dimensions $m^{-1} \cdot kg \cdot sec^{-3}$, or in watt/(sec^{-1} · m^2), with dimensions $kg \cdot sec^{-2}$;

in the cgs system, in erg/(sec · cm · cm^2), with dimensions $cm^{-1} \cdot g \cdot sec^{-3}$, or in erg/(sec · sec^{-1}· cm^2), with dimensions $g \cdot sec^{-2}$.

These units are used for measuring the spectral flux intensity of radio waves.

The spectral energy flux intensity of electromagnetic waves of shorter wavelength (x-rays, gamma rays) is usually measured in units of watt/(Å · m^2) or erg/(sec · Å · cm^2).

2. UNITS OF MEASUREMENT OF QUANTITIES OF THERMAL RADIATION

Thermal, or temperature, radiation is radiation issuing from a body heated by energy reaching it from an outside source.

Radiating bodies are described by two quantities—integral and spectral emissivity.

When thermal radiation falls on the surface of a body, the body absorbs some of the energy. Different bodies are capable of absorbing radiant energy incident upon them to different extents. This power is described by a quantity known as the *absorptivity* of a body.

Below we consider units of measurement for thermal radiation and absorption.

Integral emissivity of a body. The integral emissivity R of a radiating body is equal to the total energy, that is, the energy of all wavelengths radiated from a unit surface of the body per unit time. In other words, the integral emissivity is the integral energy flux radiated from a unit of surface of the body.

The integral emissivity is determined by the formula:

$$R = \frac{d\Phi}{dS} \qquad (6.10)$$

where $d\Phi$ is the integral energy flux emitted from the surface dS of the radiating body.

It follows from (6.10) that the integral emissivity is measured:

in the MKS system, in watt/m², with dimensions kg/sec^{-3};

in the cgs system, in erg/(cm² · sec), with dimensions g · sec^{-3}.

In practice, the integral emissivity is measured in the units cal/(cm² · sec) and watt/cm².

Spectral emissivity of a body. The spectral emissivity of a radiating body is the energy emitted from a unit surface of the body per unit time and per unit interval of wavelength near the wavelength λ.

The spectral emissivity can also be defined as the spectral energy flux from a unit surface of the body.

The spectral emissivity $r_\lambda (r_\nu)$ is determined from the equations:

$$r_\lambda = \frac{d\Phi_\lambda}{dS} \qquad (6.11)$$

$$r_\nu = \frac{d\Phi_\nu}{dS} \qquad (6.12)$$

where $d\Phi_\lambda (d\Phi_\nu)$ is the spectral flux from the surface dS of the radiating body.

It follows from Eqs. (6.11) and (6.12) that the spectral emissivity is measured:

in the MKS system, in watt/$(m \cdot m^2)$, with dimensions $m^{-1} \cdot kg \cdot sec^{-3}$, or in watt/$(m \cdot sec^{-1})$, with dimensions $kg \cdot sec^{-2}$;

in the cgs system, in erg/$(cm \cdot cm^2 \cdot sec)$, with dimensions $cm^{-1} \cdot g \cdot sec^{-3}$, or in erg/$cm^2$, with dimensions $g \cdot sec^{-2}$.

In practice, the spectral emissivity is also measured in the units watt/$(cm^2 \cdot \text{Å}$ and cal/$(cm^2 \cdot \text{Å})$.

The spectral emissivity is sometimes called the radiance and, at a given temperature, is a function of wavelength (frequency).

Absorptivity of a body. The absorptivity of a body is a quantity equal to the ratio of the radiation energy absorbed by the body to the radiation energy incident upon it. Since the proportion of energy absorbed by the body differs according to wavelength, the absorptivity must be determined for a narrow waveband close to the wavelength λ.

The absorptivity a_λ can be determined from the equation:

$$a_\lambda = \frac{dW'_\lambda}{dW_\lambda} \tag{6.13}$$

where dW'_λ is the radiation energy absorbed by the body and dW_λ is the radiation energy incident on the body (both corresponding to the waveband $d\lambda$ near the wavelength λ).

The ratio $\frac{dW'_\lambda}{dW_\lambda}$ can be replaced by the ratio of energy fluxes $\frac{d\Phi'_\lambda}{d\Phi_\lambda}$; hence, Eq. (6.13) can be written in the form:

$$a_\lambda = \frac{d\Phi'_\lambda}{d\Phi_\lambda} \tag{6.14}$$

where $d\Phi'_\lambda$ is the spectral energy flux absorbed by the body and $d\Phi_\lambda$ is the spectral energy flux incident upon it.

It follows from (6.14) that the absorptivity of a body is a dimensionless quantity and does not have any unit of measurement.

3. UNITS OF MEASUREMENT OF PHOTOMETRIC QUANTITIES

When considering photometric quantities, we have to take one distinctive feature into account. As opposed to the quantities of radiation considered above, the measurement of photometric quantities is based on the physiological action of light and is, therefore, to a considerable extent a subjective evaluation. This is due to the fact that radiations of different wavelengths give rise to different optical impressions. This distinction is, on the one hand, qualitative (that is, different wavelengths cause different color sensations), while on the other hand, it is quantitative (that is, different wavelengths cause visual sensations of varying intensity). The most powerful sensation of light (at constant radiant energy flux) is produced by the wavelength λ = 555 mμ. Radiant energy at other wavelengths in the visible region of the spectrum produces less impression. Radiant energy with a wavelength greater than 0.76 μ or less than 0.4 μ is not visible at all.

The subjective nature of photometric quantities is also manifested in the fact that people perceive different areas of the spectrum in different ways. Hence, when measuring photometric quantities, we have to start with a so-called "average" sensitivity of the eye. Such an "average" is established by comparison of the individual sensitivity of the eyes of a large number of people who do not suffer from defective vision.

The mean sensitivity of the eye is described by a particular quantity known as the *visibility factor*.

Below we consider the units of measurement of photometric quantities.

Candlepower of source. The candlepower of a source is a quantity determining the energy radiated by the source per unit time, rated on the basis of its lighting effect.

The unit of candlepower is the *candle*.

The candle (c) is the luminous intensity of 1/60 square centimeter of black body radiation operating at the temperature of solidification of platinum.

This new candle is related, in the following manner, to the international candle (the unit previously in use).

1 international candle = 1.005 new candles;
1 new candle = 0.995 international candles.

Luminous flux. The luminous flux emitted by a light source in a solid angle $d\omega$ is the quantity numerically equal to the product of the candlepower I of the source and the solid angle, that is:

$$dF = Id\omega. \qquad (6.15)$$

Assuming, in this formula, that I = 1 c and $d\omega$ = 1 steradian, we can find the unit of measurement of luminous flux. This unit is called the lumen.

The lumen (lm) is the luminous flux which is emitted by an isotropic point source of 1 candle in a solid angle of 1 steradian. When defined in this way, the lumen is related to the international lumen in the following way:

1 international lumen = 1.005 new lumens;
1 new lumen = 0.995 international lumens.

It follows from Eq. (6.15) that the total luminous flux emitted by a source of candlepower I is equal to:

$$F = 4\pi I \qquad (6.16)$$

The luminous flux can also be defined in the following way: the luminous flux through a surface dS is the energy transferred through the surface by radiation per unit time, as evaluated by its visual impression.

Visibility factor. The visibility factor V_λ is the ratio of the luminous flux F to the radiant energy flux Φ_λ producing this luminous flux, that is:

$$V_\lambda = \frac{F}{\Phi_\lambda} \qquad (6.17)$$

In this equation, the energy flux Φ_λ describes light as a physical phenomenon, while the luminous flux F describes it as a psycho-physical phenomenon.

The quantity Φ_λ shows how much energy passes through a surface per unit of time, and F shows how much of an impression the light energy makes on a human eye.

Thus, the visibility factor is a quantity relating the characteristics of light as both a physical and a psycho-physical phenomenon.

The visibility factor is a subjective quantity. The numerical value of the factor is different for different people, and, even for the same eye, the visibility factor varies according to wavelength.

For the average eye, the greatest visibility factor occurs at a wavelength $\lambda = 550$ mμ. For wavelengths greater than 760 mμ or less than 400 mμ the visibility factor is zero.

It follows from Eq. (6.17) that the visibility factor is measured in lm/watt or lm/(erg/sec).

Illumination of a surface. The illumination I is determined by the luminous flux incident on a unit area. It follows from the definition that:

$$E = \frac{dF}{dS} \qquad (6.18)$$

The units of measurement of illumination are the lux (lm/m^2) and the phot (lm/cm^2).

The *lux* is the illumination produced by a luminous flux of 1 lumen uniformly distributed over an area of 1 m^2.

The *phot* is the illumination produced by a luminous flux of 1 lumen uniformly distributed over an area of 1 cm^2.

The lux and the phot are related in the following way:

$$1 \text{ lux} = 1\,\frac{\text{lm}}{\text{m}^2} = 1 \cdot \frac{\text{lm}}{10^4 \text{ cm}^2} = 10^{-4}\,\frac{\text{lm}}{\text{cm}^2} = 10^{-4} \text{ phot}$$

Thus:

$$1 \text{ lux} = 10^{-4} \text{ phot}$$
$$1 \text{ phot} = 10^4 \text{ lux}$$

Emittance. The emittance R is defined as the quantity of luminous flux emitted per unit area of a radiating surface, that is:

$$R = \frac{dF}{dS} \tag{6.19}$$

where dF is the total luminous flux emitted from the area dS.

Comparison of Eqs. (6.18) and (6.19) shows that emittance should be measured in the same units as illumination, that is, in luxes and phots.

Brightness. Brightness is a quantity describing the emittance of a body in a given direction. The brightness B is defined as the quantity of luminous flux radiated in a given direction by a unit illuminating surface in a solid angle of 1 steradian.

Brightness can also be defined as the ratio of the candlepower in a given direction to the projection of the illuminating surface onto a plane perpendicular to the given direction.

Brightness is determined from the formula:

$$B = \frac{dF}{S \cos \varphi \, d\omega} \tag{6.20}$$

where dF is the luminous flux emitted from an area S, $d\omega$ is the solid angle within which the flux is emitted, φ is the angle between the normal to the area and the direction of emittance, and $S \cos \varphi$ is the projection of the area S onto the direction determined by the angle φ.

The units of brightness are the stilb and the nit.

The *stilb* (c/cm^2) is the brightness of a surface, one square centimeter of which radiates one candle in a direction perpendicular to the surface.

The *nit* (c/m^2) is the brightness of a surface, one square meter of which radiates one candle in a direction perpendicular to the surface.

The stilb and the nit are related in the following way:

$$1 \text{ stilb} = \frac{1 \text{ c}}{1 \text{ cm}^2} = \frac{1 \text{ c}}{(10^{-2} \text{ m})^2} = 10^4 \frac{\text{c}}{\text{m}^2} = 10^4 \text{ nit}$$

$$1 \text{ stilb} = 10^4 \text{ nit}$$

4. UNITS OF MEASUREMENT OF QUANTITIES OF RADIOACTIVE DECAY

When the nuclei of radioactive matter decay, three types of radiation are emitted: alpha, beta, and gamma radiation. Alpha radiation is composed of positively charged helium nuclei, beta radiation consists of a flow of electrons or positrons, and gamma radiation consists of electromagnetic rays with a wavelength less than 1 Å.

Radioactive decay is described by the following quantities: the decay constant, half-life period, radioactivity, specific radioactivity, and concentration of radioactive matter in a given medium (water, air, etc.).

Below we consider the units of measurement of these quantities.

Decay constant. The decay constant is a quantity equal to the proportion of radioactive atoms decaying in 1 sec. The unit of measurement of the decay constant λ can be determined from the equation:

$$dN = -\lambda N dt \qquad (6.21)$$

where N is the number of atoms in the radioactive substance at the beginning of the time interval dt, and dN is the number of atoms which decay over the time dt. From this equation, we find that:

$$\lambda = -\frac{dN}{N dt} \qquad (6.22)$$

If we consider the fact that dN/N is a dimensionless quantity, it follows from (6.22) that the decay constant is measured in sec^{-1}.

Half-life. The half-life τ is the time in which half the nuclei of a radioactive material decay. The half-life is measured in time units, that is, in seconds, minutes, hours, or years.

Radioactivity. The radioactivity of a substance is the number of atoms which decay per second in a given radioactive preparation. It follows from Eq. (6.21) that the radioactivity:

$$a = \frac{dN}{dt} = -\lambda N \qquad (6.23)$$

that is, the radioactivity is proportional to the amount of radioactive matter in the given preparation. Hence, measuring the radioactivity is actually the same as measuring the amount of radioactive matter (the two quantities are directly proportional).

The radioactivity of a preparation, in terms of α and β decay, is measured in curies or rutherfords.

The *curie* is the amount of radioactive substance which undergoes exactly $3.7 \cdot 10^{10}$ decays a second.

The curie is used to form the fractional units millicurie and microcurie.

1 millicurie = 10^{-3} curie,

1 microcurie = 10^{-6} curie.

The *rutherford* is the amount of radioactive matter which undergoes 10^6 decays a second.

The curie and rutherford are related in the following way:

1 curie = $3.7 \cdot 10^4$ rutherfords,

1 rutherford = $2.7 \cdot 10^{-5}$ curies.

The activity of a preparation in terms of gamma rays is measured in gram-equivalents of radium.

The gram-equivalent of radium is the amount of radioactive matter which produces gamma radiation equivalent to the action of 1 gram of radium under the same measuring conditions.

The gram-equivalent of radium is used to form a fractional unit, the milligram-equivalent radium.

One milligram-equivalent of radium = 10^{-3} gram-equivalent of radium.

Specific activity. The specific activity of a substance is equal to the number of nuclei decaying in 1 sec in 1 gram of radioactive matter. The specific activity is measured in curies per gram (curie/g) or rutherfords per gram (rutherford/g).

The curie per gram (curie/g) is the specific activity of a substance in which $3.7 \cdot 10^{10}$ atoms decay per second per gram of substance.

The rutherford per gram (rutherford/g) is the specific activity of a substance in which 10^6 atoms decay per second per gram.

Radioactive concentration. The concentration of radioactive material in any medium (air, water, etc.) is termed the quantity of radioactive matter per cm^3 of medium.

The units of concentration of radioactive matter are curie/cm^3, curie/liter, *eman*, and *mache*.

The curie/cm^3 is the concentration at which there is 1 curie of radioactive matter in 1 cm of medium. The curie/l is defined in a similar way.

1 eman = 10^{-13} curie/cm^3,

1 mache = 3.64 emans = $3.64 \cdot 10^{-13}$ curie/cm^3.

5. UNITS OF MEASUREMENT OF QUANTITIES CHARACTERIZING THE INTERACTION BETWEEN RADIATION AND MATTER

The passage of x-rays, gamma rays, and also corpuscular radiation (alpha and beta rays, neutrons) through matter is accompanied by ionization of the atoms in the matter.

During ionization, some of the radiation energy is lost. This phenomenon is termed absorption of radiation energy by the matter.

The degree of ionization of a substance and the amount of radiation energy absorbed by it are indications of interaction between the radiation and the matter, and form the basis of the quantities introduced to describe this effect.

Below we consider the units of measurement of quantities describing the interaction between radiation and matter.

Absorbed dose. The absorbed dose (simply dose) is the amount of radiation energy absorbed by 1 cm^3 (or by 1 g) of a medium through which radiation has passed. The absorbed dose is denoted by D.

When calculating the amount of radiation energy absorbed per unit of volume or area of a specific medium, we use the *roentgen* as the unit; when calculating per unit mass of medium, we use the *rad*.

"The roentgen (r) is the dose of x-ray or gamma radiation such that an associated corpuscular emission per 0.001293 g of air produces, in air, ions carrying a charge of 1 electrostatic unit of quantity of electricity of either sign."

The number 0.001293 g corresponds to the mass of 1 cm^3 of air at 0°C and normal atmospheric pressure.

The expression "associated corpuscular emission...produces, in air, ions..." means the following. When passing through a substance, x-rays and gamma radiation do not directly ionize it. Their action can be reduced to the creation of a corpuscular emission (in the form of a high-speed electron flow) inside the substance itself. The collisions between electrons and atoms cause the ionization which is observed in the substance when x-rays and gamma rays pass through it.

The roentgen forms fractional units—the milliroentgen and the microroentgen:

$$1 \text{ mr} = 10^{-3} \text{ r}; \ 1 \ \mu\text{r} = 10^{-6}\text{r}$$

The roentgen and the fractional units formed from it are used only with regard to the dosage of x-rays and gamma rays, that is, to determine the dosage of electromagnetic radiation.

Measurement of the dosage of corpuscular radiation (alpha and beta rays, neutrons, etc.) is made in units called *reps* (roentgen, equivalent, physical).*

The rep is the dose of ionizing radiation at which the energy absorbed by a substance is equal to the loss in energy during ionization caused by 1 r of x-ray or gamma radiation.

In physical reactions, 1 rep of corpuscular radiation is equal to 1 r of electromagnetic radiation.

Over the last few years a new unit of dosage, the *rad*, has come into common use.

The rad is a dose of ionized radiation at which 1 gram of irradiated material absorbs 100 ergs of energy.

In order to establish the relationship between the rad and the roentgen, we have to calculate the amount of energy which is absorbed by one g of a medium when the radiation dose is 1 r. Comparison of this energy with 100 ergs of energy yields the ratio between the rad and the roentgen.

It follows from the definition of the roentgen that a dose of 1 r corresponds to the energy required to produce, in 0.001293 g of air, the exact number of pairs of ions such that the total (positive or negative) charge equals 1 statcoulomb.

---

*The unit is also termed the pherphysical equivalent of a roentgen.

In order to compute the number of pairs of ions, we use the relationship:

$$n = \frac{q}{e} = \frac{1 \text{ statcoulomb}}{4.8 \cdot 10^{-10} \text{ statcoulomb}} = 2.08 \cdot 10^9 \text{ pairs of ions}$$

where e is the elementary charge (electron charge).

According to the definition of the roentgen, this is the number of pairs of ions formed in a mass of 0.001293 g of air. Consequently, at a dose of 1 r, 1 gram of air forms:

$$\frac{2.08 \cdot 10^9}{0.001293} = 1.61 \cdot 10^{12} \text{ pairs of ions}$$

But to form one pair of ions we require, as is well known, about 32.5 ev or $32.5 \cdot 1.60 \cdot 10^{-12} = 5.2 \cdot 10^{-11}$ erg. Thus, the energy required to form $1.61 \cdot 10^{12}$ pairs of ions is:

$$5.2 \cdot 10^{-11} \cdot 1.61 \cdot 10^{12} = 84 \text{ ergs}$$

Thus, a dose of 1 r absorbed by 1 g of air corresponds to 84 ergs/g.

Comparing this energy with the energy absorbed by 1 g of air at a dose of 1 rad (that is, with 100 ergs/g), we find that:

$$1 \text{ r} = \frac{84}{100} = 0.84 \text{ rad}$$

$$1 \text{ rad} = \frac{100}{84} = 1.2 \text{ r}$$

These relationships are only valid when determining the absorption of x-rays and gamma radiation in air.

When x-rays and gamma rays pass through other substances, the relationship between the roentgen and the rad is different, since different substances absorb energy to different extents. For example, when x-rays pass through water, 1 gram absorbs 93 ergs/g. Consequently, for water the relationship between the roentgen and the rad is:

$$1 \text{ r} = \frac{93}{100} = 0.93 \text{ rad}$$

$$1 \text{ rad} = \frac{100}{93} = 1.1 \text{ r}$$

X-rays, gamma rays, and corpuscular radiation affect human tissue. This effect is known as the biological effect of radiation. The biological action of radiation is not only a function of the absorbed dose (in the physical sense), but also depends on the type of radiation; that is, the biological effect of different radiations is not equivalent. Hence the biological effect of radiation cannot be measured in the above-described units of dosage—roentgens, reps, and rads.

The unit of biological effect of radiation is the EBR (equivalent biological roentgen). The EBR is the dose of radiation (of any type), which, when absorbed by human tissue, produces a biological effect equivalent to the action of 1 r of x-rays or gamma rays.

To find the value of this radiation, we must express the dosage in reps, multiplied by the coefficient of relative biological intensity k:

$$D(\text{EBR}) = kD \text{ (rep)} \tag{6.24}$$

The coefficient k differs with the type of radiation. For example,
k = 1 for x-rays and gamma and beta radiation,
k = 20 for alpha radiation,
k = 10 for protons.

Integral absorbed dose. The integral absorbed dose or integral dose is the radiation energy absorbed throughout the volume under consideration. The integral dose W can be determined from the equation:

$$W = kmD \tag{6.25}$$

where D is the radiation dose, m is the mass of the substance for which we are determining the dose, and k is the proportionality factor.

Assuming, in this equation, that k = 1, m = 1 g and D = 1 rad, we find the unit of measurement of the integral dose is 1 g · rad.

Since 1 rad = 100 ergs/g, we obtain:

$$1 \text{ g} \cdot \text{rad} = 100 \text{ ergs}$$

Absorbed dose rate. The absorbed dose rate is a quantity equal to the dose absorbed per unit time; that is, it is determined by the ratio:

$$P = \frac{D}{t} \tag{6.26}$$

where D is the dose and t is the time over which it is received.

It follows from (6.26) that the dose rate is measured in units of r/sec, r/min, or r/hr; or also, accordingly, rad/sec, rad/min, or rad/hr.

Integral absorbed dose rate. The integral absorbed dose rate is the radiation energy absorbed by the entire volume under investigation, per unit time. It is calculated from the equation:

$$N = \frac{W}{t} \tag{6.27}$$

We can see from this equation that the unit of integral absorbed dose rate is the (g · rad)/sec or erg/sec, and that:

$$1 \frac{\text{g} \cdot \text{rad}}{\text{sec}} = 100 \frac{\text{ergs}}{\text{sec}}$$

In conclusion, let us illustrate the determination of the activity of a radioactive preparation.

Example. The half-life period of plutonium Pu^{239} is $2.41 \cdot 10^4$ years. Determine, in curies, the activity of a mixture containing 8.5 g of plutonium and also the specific activity of this isotope in millicuries/g.

Solution. The activity a of the mixture, that is, the number of decays occurring in 1 second, is determined from the equation:

$$a = \frac{dN}{dt} = \lambda N \qquad (1)$$

where N is the number of radioactive atoms in the mixture and λ is the decay constant.

The decay constant can be expressed in terms of the half-life, which we are given:

$$\lambda = \frac{\ln 2}{T} = \frac{0.693}{T} \qquad (2)$$

The number of radioactive atoms in the mixture can be expressed in terms of its mass m, Avogadro's number N_0, and its atomic weight A, as follows:

$$N = \frac{m}{A} N_0 \qquad (3)$$

Substituting λ from (2) and N from (3) into (1), we obtain:

$$a = 0.693 \frac{m N_0}{AT} \qquad (4)$$

Let us write down the numerical values of the quantities contained in (4):

$$m = 8.5 \text{ g}$$
$$N_0 = 6.02 \cdot 10^{23} \text{ mole}^{-1}$$
$$A = 239 \frac{\text{g}}{\text{mole}}$$
$$T = 2.41 \cdot 10^4 \text{ years} = 2.41 \cdot 10^4 \cdot 3.16 \cdot 10^7 \text{ sec}$$

Substituting these values into (4), we obtain:

$$a = \frac{0.693 \cdot 8.5 \cdot 6.02 \cdot 10^{23}}{239 \cdot 2.41 \cdot 10^4 \cdot 3.16 \cdot 10^7} = 1.95 \cdot 10^{10} \text{ sec}^{-1}$$

In order to express the radioactivity in curies, the derived number of decays per second must be divided by $3.7 \cdot 10^{10}$, that is:

$$a = \frac{1.95 \cdot 10^{10}}{3.7 \cdot 10^{10}} = 0.53 \text{ curies}$$

The specific rate of activity a of a radioactive isotope is the activity of 1 gram of the mixture, so that:

$$a_{sp} = \frac{a}{m}$$

Substituting the numerical values into this equation:

$$a = 0.53 \text{ curies}, \quad m = 8.5 \text{ g}$$

we obtain:

$$a_{sp} = \frac{0.53}{8.5} = 0.062 \frac{\text{curies}}{\text{g}} = 62 \frac{\text{millicuries}}{\text{g}}$$

TABLES OF RELATIONSHIPS AMONG UNITS OF MEASUREMENT OF PHYSICAL QUANTITIES AND IMPORTANT CONSTANTS

Table 1
Units of Mass

Unit of measurement		Systems of units					Other units	
		Metric system			British system			
		g	kg	Metric slug	lbm (pound)	Slug	Metric ton	amu (atomic mass unit)
Metric system	1 g	1	10^{-3}	$1.02 \cdot 10^{-4}$	$2.205 \cdot 10^{-3}$	$6.82 \cdot 10^{-5}$	10^{-6}	$6.02 \cdot 10^{23}$
	1 kg	10^3	1	0.102	2.205	$6.82 \cdot 10^{-2}$	10^{-3}	—
	1 metric slug	$9.81 \cdot 10^3$	9.81	1	21.6	0.67	$9.81 \cdot 10^{-3}$	—
British system	1 lbm	454	0.454	$4.63 \cdot 10^{-2}$	1	0.031	$4.54 \cdot 10^{-4}$	—
	1 slug	$14.6 \cdot 10^3$	14.6	1.49	32.174	1	$14.6 \cdot 10^{-3}$	—
Other units	1 metric ton	10^6	10^3	102	$2.205 \cdot 10^3$	68.2	1	—
	1 amu	$1.66 \cdot 10^{-24}$	—	—	—	—	—	1

Table 2
Units of Force

Unit of measurement		Metric system			British system	
		Dyne	Newton	kgf	pdl (poundal)	lbf (pound)
Metric system	1 dyne	1	10^{-5}	$1.02 \cdot 10^{-6}$	$7.23 \cdot 10^{-5}$	$2.24 \cdot 10^{-6}$
	1 N	10^5	1	0.102	7.23	0.224
	1 kgf	$9.81 \cdot 10^5$	9.81	1	70.9	2.20
British system	1 pdl	$1.38 \cdot 10^4$	0.138	$1.41 \cdot 10^{-2}$	1	0.031
	p lbf	$4.44 \cdot 10^5$	4.44	0.453	32,174	1

Table 3

Units of

Unit of measurement		Metric system			British system	
		erg	joule	kgfm	ft-pdl	ft-lbf
Metric system	1 erg	1	10^{-7}	$1.02 \cdot 10^{-8}$	$2.37 \cdot 10^{-6}$	$7.38 \cdot 10^{-8}$
	1 joule	10^7	1	0.102	23.7	0.738
	1 kgfm	$9.81 \cdot 10^7$	9.81	1	233	7.23
British system	1 foot-poundal	$4.21 \cdot 10^5$	0.042	$4.30 \cdot 10^{-3}$	1	0.031
	1 foot-pound	$1.36 \cdot 10^7$	1.36	0.138	32.174	1
Other units	1 kilojoule	10^{10}	10^3	102	$2.37 \cdot 10^4$	738
	1 watt-hr	$3.6 \cdot 10^{10}$	$3.6 \cdot 10^3$	367	$8.53 \cdot 10^4$	$2.66 \cdot 10^3$
	1 kilowatt-hr	$3.6 \cdot 10^{13}$	$3.6 \cdot 10^6$	$3.67 \cdot 10^5$	$8.53 \cdot 10^7$	$2.66 \cdot 10^6$
	1 BTU	$1.06 \cdot 10^{10}$	$1.06 \cdot 10^3$	108	$2.5 \cdot 10^4$	778
	1 cal	$4.18 \cdot 10^7$	4.18	0.427	99.3	3.09
	1 kcal	$4.18 \cdot 10^{10}$	$4.18 \cdot 10^3$	427	$9.93 \cdot 10^4$	$3.09 \cdot 10^3$
	1 liter-atm.	$1.013 \cdot 10^9$	$1.013 \cdot 10^2$	10.33	$2.4 \cdot 10^3$	74.7

Table 4

Units of

Unit of measurement		Metric system		
		$\dfrac{erg}{sec}$	watt	$\dfrac{kgfm}{sec}$
Metric system	$1\dfrac{erg}{sec}$	1	10^{-7}	$1.02 \cdot 10^{-8}$
	1 watt	10^7	1	0.102
	$1\dfrac{kgfm}{sec}$	$9.81 \cdot 10^7$	9.81	1
Other units	1 kw	10^{10}	10^3	102
	1 metric horsepower	$7.36 \cdot 10^9$	736	75
	1 ft-pound per sec	$1.36 \cdot 10^7$	1.36	0.139
	1 horsepower	$7.45 \cdot 10^9$	745.2	76.5

Work (Energy)

	Other units					
kilojoule	wh	kwh	BTU	cal	kcal	l.-atm.
10^{-10}	$2.78 \cdot 10^{-11}$	$2.78 \cdot 10^{-14}$	$9.48 \cdot 10^{-11}$	$2.39 \cdot 10^{-8}$	$2.39 \cdot 10^{-11}$	$9.87 \cdot 10^{-10}$
10^{-3}	$2.78 \cdot 10^{-4}$	$2.78 \cdot 10^{-7}$	$9.48 \cdot 10^{-4}$	0.239	$2.39 \cdot 10^{-4}$	$9.87 \cdot 10^{-3}$
$9.81 \cdot 10^{-3}$	$2.73 \cdot 10^{-3}$	$2.73 \cdot 10^{-6}$	$9.30 \cdot 10^{-3}$	2.34	$2.34 \cdot 10^{-3}$	$9.68 \cdot 10^{-2}$
$4.21 \cdot 10^{-5}$	$1.17 \cdot 10^{-5}$	$1.17 \cdot 10^{-8}$	$4.00 \cdot 10^{-5}$	$1.01 \cdot 10^{-2}$	$1.01 \cdot 10^{-5}$	$4.16 \cdot 10^{-4}$
$1.36 \cdot 10^{-3}$	$3.77 \cdot 10^{-4}$	$3.77 \cdot 10^{-7}$	$1.29 \cdot 10^{-3}$	0.324	$3.24 \cdot 10^{-4}$	0.013
1	0.278	$2.78 \cdot 10^{-4}$	0.948	239	0.239	9.87
3.6	1	10^{-3}	3.41	859	0.859	35.4
$3.6 \cdot 10^3$	10^3	1	$3.41 \cdot 10^3$	$8.59 \cdot 10^5$	859	$3.54 \cdot 10^4$
1.06	0.293	$2.93 \cdot 10^{-4}$	1	252	0.252	10.4
$4.18 \cdot 10^{-3}$	$1.16 \cdot 10^{-3}$	$1.16 \cdot 10^{-6}$	$3.97 \cdot 10^{-3}$	1	10^{-3}	$4.13 \cdot 10^{-2}$
4.18	1.16	$1.16 \cdot 10^{-3}$	3.97	10^3	1	41.3
0.1013	$2.8 \cdot 10^{-2}$	$2.8 \cdot 10^{-5}$	0.096	24.2	$2.42 \cdot 10^{-2}$	1

Power

	Other units		
kw	Metric horsepower	$\dfrac{\text{ft-lbf}}{\text{sec}}$	Horsepower
10^{-10}	$1.36 \cdot 10^{-10}$	$7.38 \cdot 10^{-8}$	$1.34 \cdot 10^{-10}$
10^{-3}	$1.36 \cdot 10^{-3}$	0.738	$1.34 \cdot 10^{-3}$
$9.81 \cdot 10^{-3}$	$1.33 \cdot 10^{-2}$	7.24	$1.31 \cdot 10^{-2}$
1	1.36	$7.38 \cdot 10^2$	1.34
0.736	1	—	0.986
$1.36 \cdot 10^{-3}$	—	1	$1.82 \cdot 10^{-3}$
0.745	1.01	550	1

Table 5
Units of Pressure

Unit of measurement	Metric system			Other units					
	Barye = $\frac{dyne}{cm^2}$	$\frac{Newton}{m^2}$	$\frac{kgf}{m^2}$	Pieza	Physical atmosphere	Technical atmosphere	mm Hg	$\frac{lbf}{ft^2}$	$\frac{lbf}{in^2}$
Metric system 1 barye	1	0.1	$1.02 \cdot 10^{-2}$	10^{-4}	$9.87 \cdot 10^{-7}$	$1.02 \cdot 10^{-6}$	$7.5 \cdot 10^{-4}$	$2.09 \cdot 10^{-3}$	$1.45 \cdot 10^{-5}$
1 $\frac{N}{m^2}$	10	1	0.102	10^{-3}	$9.87 \cdot 10^{-6}$	$1.02 \cdot 10^{-5}$	$7.5 \cdot 10^{-3}$	$2.09 \cdot 10^{-2}$	$1.45 \cdot 10^{-4}$
1 $\frac{kgf}{m^2}$	98.1	9.81	1	$9.81 \cdot 10^{-3}$	$9.68 \cdot 10^{-5}$	10^{-4}	$7.36 \cdot 10^{-2}$	0.205	$1.42 \cdot 10^{-3}$
Other units 1 pieza	10^4	10^3	102	1	$9.87 \cdot 10^{-3}$	$1.02 \cdot 10^{-2}$	7.5	—	—
1 phys. atm	$1.013 \cdot 10^6$	$1.013 \cdot 10^5$	$1.033 \cdot 10^4$	$1.013 \cdot 10^2$	1	1.033	760	2116	14.696
1 tech. atm	$9.81 \cdot 10^5$	$9.81 \cdot 10^4$	10^4	98.1	0.968	1	735	—	—
1 mm Hg	$1.33 \cdot 10^3$	133	13.6	0.133	$1.31 \cdot 10^{-3}$	$1.36 \cdot 10^{-3}$	1	2.78	$1.93 \cdot 10^{-2}$
1 pound/ft²	479.0	47.9	4.88	—	$4.73 \cdot 10^{-4}$	—	0.359	1	$6.94 \cdot 10^{-3}$
1 pound/in²	$6.89 \cdot 10^4$	$6.89 \cdot 10^3$	703.0	—	0.068	—	51.7	144	1

Table 6
Units of Charge

Unit of measurement	Statcoulomb	Abcoulomb	Coulomb
1 cgs esu (q) = 1 statcoulomb	1	$3.33 \cdot 10^{-11}$	$3.33 \cdot 10^{-10}$
1 cgs emu (q) = 1 abcoulomb	$3 \cdot 10^{10}$	1	10
1 coulomb	$3 \cdot 10^{9}$	0.1	1

Table 7
Units of Electric Field Intensity

	Unit of measurement	System units			Other units
		cgs esu (E)	cgs emu (E)	volt/meter	volt/cm
System units	1 cgs esu (E)	1	$3 \cdot 10^{10}$	$3 \cdot 10^{4}$	300
System units	1 cgs emu (E)	$3.33 \cdot 10^{-11}$	1	10^{-6}	10^{-8}
System units	$1 \frac{v}{m}$	$3.33 \cdot 10^{-5}$	10^{6}	1	10^{-2}
Other units	$1 \frac{v}{cm}$	$3.33 \cdot 10^{-3}$	10^{8}	100	1

Table 8
Units of Electric Induction (Displacement)

Unit of measurement	cgs esu (D)	cgs emu (D)	MKSA (D)	MKSAr (D)
1 cgs esu (D)	1	$3.33 \cdot 10^{-11}$	$3.33 \cdot 10^{-6}$	$\frac{1}{4\pi} \cdot 3.33 \cdot 10^{-6}$
1 cgs emu (D)	$3 \cdot 10^{10}$	1	10^{5}	$\frac{1}{4\pi} \cdot 10^{5}$
1 MKSA (D)	$3 \cdot 10^{5}$	10^{-5}	1	$\frac{1}{4\pi}$
1 MKSAr (D)	$4\pi \cdot 3 \cdot 10^{5}$	$4\pi \cdot 10^{-5}$	4π	1

Table 9
Units of Electric Induction Flux

Unit of measurement	cgs esu (N)	cgs emu (N)	Coulomb	Coulomb*
1 cgs esu (N)	1	$3.33 \cdot 10^{-11}$	$3.33 \cdot 10^{-10}$	$\frac{1}{4\pi} \cdot 3.33 \cdot 10^{-10}$
1 cgs emu (N)	$3 \cdot 10^{10}$	1	10	$\frac{1}{4\pi} \cdot 10$
1 coulomb	$3 \cdot 10^{9}$	0.1	1	$\frac{1}{4\pi}$
1 coulomb*	$4\pi \cdot 3 \cdot 10^{9}$	0.4π	4π	1

Note: Here and below, asterisk (*) denotes value in rationalized MKSA (MKSAr) system.

Table 10
Units of Potential

Unit of measurement	Statvolt	Abvolt	Volt
1 cgs esu (U) = 1 statvolt	1	$3 \cdot 10^{10}$	300
1 cgs emu (U) = 1 abvolt	$3.33 \cdot 10^{-11}$	1	10^{-8}
1 volt	$3.33 \cdot 10^{-3}$	10^{8}	1

Table 11
Units of Capacitance

Unit of measurement	System units			Other units	
	cm	Abfarad	Farad	Microfarad	Picofarad
System units: 1 cgs esu (C) = 1 cm	1	$1.11 \cdot 10^{-21}$	$1.11 \cdot 10^{-21}$	$1.11 \cdot 10^{-6}$	1.11
1 cgs emu (C) = 1 abfarad	$9 \cdot 10^{20}$	1	10^{9}	10^{15}	10^{21}
1 farad	$9 \cdot 10^{11}$	10^{-9}	1	10^{6}	10^{12}
Other units: 1 microfarad	$9 \cdot 10^{5}$	10^{-15}	10^{-6}	1	10^{6}
1 picofarad	0.9	10^{-21}	10^{-12}	10^{-6}	1

Table 12
Units of Current

Unit of measurement	System units			Other units	
	Statampere	Abampere	Amp	Milliamp	Microamp
System units 1 cgs esu *(I)* = 1 statampere	1	$3.33 \cdot 10^{-11}$	$3.33 \cdot 10^{-10}$	$3.33 \cdot 10^{-7}$	$3.33 \cdot 10^{-4}$
1 cgs emu *(I)* = 1 abampere	$3 \cdot 10^{10}$	1	10	10^4	10^7
1 amp	$3 \cdot 10^9$	0.1	1	10^3	10^6
Other units 1 milliamp	$3 \cdot 10^6$	10^{-4}	10^{-3}	1	10^3
1 microamp	$3 \cdot 10^3$	10^{-7}	10^{-6}	10^{-3}	1

Table 13
Units of Resistance

Unit of measurement	System units			Other units	
	Statohm	Abohm	Ohm	kohm	Megohm
System units 1 cgs esu *(R)* = 1 statohm	1	$9 \cdot 10^{20}$	$9 \cdot 10^{11}$	$9 \cdot 10^8$	$9 \cdot 10^5$
1 cgs emu *(R)* = 1 abohm	$1.11 \cdot 10^{-21}$	1	10^{-9}	10^{-12}	10^{-15}
1 ohm	$1.11 \cdot 10^{-12}$	10^9	1	10^{-3}	10^{-6}
Other units 1 kohm	$1.11 \cdot 10^{-9}$	10^{12}	10^3	1	10^{-3}
1 megohm	$1.11 \cdot 10^{-6}$	10^{15}	10^6	10^3	1

Table 14
Units of Magnetic Field Strength

Unit of measurement	Statoersted	Oersted	$\dfrac{Amp}{meter}$	$\dfrac{Amp*}{meter}$
1 cgs esu *(H)* = 1 statoersted	1	$3.33 \cdot 10^{-11}$	$3.33 \cdot 10^{-8}$	$\frac{1}{4\pi} \cdot 3.33 \cdot 10^{-8}$
1 orested	$3 \cdot 10^{10}$	1	10^3	$\frac{1}{4\pi} \cdot 10^3$
$1 \dfrac{amp}{meter}$	$3 \cdot 10^7$	10^{-3}	1	$\frac{1}{4\pi}$
$1 \dfrac{amp*}{meter}$	$3 \cdot 4\pi \cdot 10^7$	$4\pi \cdot 10^{-3}$	4π	1

Table 15
Units of Magnetic Induction

Unit of measurement	cgs esu (B)	Gauss	$\dfrac{Weber}{m^2}$
1 cgs esu (B)	1	$3 \cdot 10^{10}$	$3 \cdot 10^{6}$
1 gauss	$0.33 \cdot 10^{-10}$	1	10^{-4}
1 $\dfrac{weber}{m^2}$	$0.33 \cdot 10^{-6}$	10^{4}	1

Table 16
Units of Magnetic Induction Flux

Unit of measurement	cgs esu (Φ)	Maxwell	Weber (volt·sec)
1 cgs esu (Φ)	1	$3 \cdot 10^{10}$	300
1 maxwell	$3.33 \cdot 10^{-11}$	1	10^{-8}
1 weber (volt·sec)	$3.33 \cdot 10^{-3}$	10^{8}	1

Table 17
Units of Inductance

Unit of measurement	Stathenry	cm	Henry
1 cgs esu (L) = 1 stathenry	1	$9 \cdot 10^{20}$	$9 \cdot 10^{11}$
1 cm	$1.11 \cdot 10^{-21}$	1	10^{-9}
1 henry	$1.11 \cdot 10^{-12}$	10^{9}	1

Table 18
Values of ϵ_0 and μ_0 in Different Systems of Units

Name of quantity	MKSA	MKSAr	cgs esu	cgs emu	cgs (Gaussian)
Dielectric constant ϵ_0	$1.1 \cdot 10^{-10}\ \dfrac{f}{m}$	$8.8 \cdot 10^{-12}\ \dfrac{f}{m}$ *	1	$1.1 \cdot 10^{-21}\ cm^{-2} \cdot sec^{2}$	1
Magnetic constant μ_0	$10^{-7}\ \dfrac{h}{m}$	$1.3 \cdot 10^{-6}\ \dfrac{h}{m}$ *	$1.1 \cdot 10^{-21}\ cm^{-2} sec^{2}$	1	1

Appendix II

Important Constants

Name	Symbol	Value (more exact)	Approximate value (generally used in solution of problems)	Unit of measurement or dimensions
Absolute zero temperature	T_0	-273.16	-273	°C
Avogadro's number (number of molecules in 1 mole)	N	$6.0238 \cdot 10^{23}$	$6.02 \cdot 10^{23}$	$mole^{-1}$
Normal atmosphere	—	$1.013246 \cdot 10^6$	$1.01 \cdot 10^6$	$dyne \cdot cm^{-2}$
Boltzmann constant	k	$1.380257 \cdot 10^{-16}$	$1.38 \cdot 10^{-16}$	$erg \cdot deg^{-1}$
Wien constant	C	0.2897	0.29	$cm \cdot deg$
Gas constant (universal)	R	$8.315 \cdot 10^7$	$8.31 \cdot 10^7$	$erg \cdot deg^{-1} \cdot mole^{-1}$
		1.987	1.99	$cal \cdot deg^{-1} \cdot mole^{-1}$
		0.08206	0.082	$liter \cdot atm \cdot deg^{-1} \cdot mole^{-1}$
		0.848	0.848	$kgfm \cdot deg^{-1} \cdot mole^{-1}$
Gravitational constant	γ	$6.67 \cdot 10^{-8}$	$6.67 \cdot 10^{-8}$	$cm^3 \cdot g^{-1} \cdot sec^{-2}$
Charge of the electron	e	$4.8025 \cdot 10^{-10}$	$4.8 \cdot 10^{-10}$	statcoulomb
		$1.601864 \cdot 10^{-19}$	$1.6 \cdot 10^{-19}$	coulomb
Ionization potential of hydrogen	U	13.527	13.5	ev
Coefficient of expansion for ideal gases	α	0.00366	$\frac{1}{273}$	deg^{-1}
Loschmidt number (number of molecules in 1 cm³ of an ideal gas under normal conditions)	n_0	$2.687 \cdot 10^{19}$	$2.69 \cdot 10^{19}$	cm^{-3}

Mass of an α-particle*	m	$6.6444 \cdot 10^{-24}$	$6.64 \cdot 10^{-24}$**	g
Mass of a hydrogen atom		$1.6734 \cdot 10^{-24}$	$1.67 \cdot 10^{-24}$	g
Mass of a neutron		$1.6749 \cdot 10^{-24}$	$1.67 \cdot 10^{-24}$	g
Mass of a proton		$1.6724 \cdot 10^{-24}$	$1.67 \cdot 10^{-24}$	g
Mass of an electron		$9.106 \cdot 10^{-28}$	$9.1 \cdot 10^{-28}$	g
Mechanical equivalent of heat	J	$4.182 \cdot 10^{7}$	$4.18 \cdot 10^{7}$	erg $\cdot$ cal^{-1}
		4.182	4.18	joule $\cdot$ cal^{-1}
		427	427	kgfm $\cdot$ kcal^{-1}
Volume of a mole of ideal gas under normal conditions	V_0	22.415	22.4	liter $\cdot$ mole^{-1}
Ratio of the mass of a hydrogen atom to the mass of the electron	—	1837.5	1840	—
Ratio of the charge of an electron to its mass	$\dfrac{e}{m}$	$5.273 \cdot 10^{17}$	$5.27 \cdot 10^{17}$	cm$^{3/2} \cdot$ g$^{-1/2} \cdot$ sec^{-1}
Ratio of the energy of a particle to its mass	$\dfrac{W}{m} = c^2$	$8.98656 \cdot 10^{20}$	$9 \cdot 10^{20}$	erg $\cdot$ g^{-1} = cm$^2 \cdot$ sec^{-2}
Planck's constant	h	$6.62377 \cdot 10^{-27}$	$6.62 \cdot 10^{-27}$	erg $\cdot$ sec
Density of mercury under normal conditions	ρ	13.59504	13.6	g $\cdot$ cm^{-3}
Radius of the first orbital in the Bohr hydrogen atom	a_1	$0.5291 \cdot 10^{-8}$	$0.529 \cdot 10^{-8}$	cm
Rydberg constant	R	$109{,}677.681$	$110{,}000$	cm^{-1}
Speed of sound in dry air under normal conditions	v	331.36	331	m $\cdot$ sec^{-1}
Speed of light in a vacuum	c	$2.99776 \cdot 10^{10}$	$3 \cdot 10^{10}$	cm $\cdot$ sec^{-1}
Stefan-Boltzmann constant	σ	$5.672 \cdot 10^{-5}$	$5.67 \cdot 10^{-5}$	erg $\cdot$ cm$^{-2} \cdot$ sec$^{-1} \cdot$ deg^{-4}
		$1.365 \cdot 10^{-12}$	$1.37 \cdot 10^{-12}$	cal $\cdot$ cm$^{-2} \cdot$ sec$^{-1} \cdot$ deg^{-4}
Heat equivalent of work	W	$0.239 \cdot 10^{-7}$	$0.24 \cdot 10^{-7}$	cal $\cdot$ erg^{-1}
		0.239	0.24	cal $\cdot$ joule^{-1}
Acceleration of gravity (normal)	g	$980{,}665$	981	cm $\cdot$ sec^{-2}
		9.80665	9.81	m $\cdot$ sec^{-2}
Faraday constant	F	$96{,}493$	$96{,}500$	coulomb $\cdot$ g-equivalent^{-1}
Electrochemical equivalent of silver	k	$1.118 \cdot 10^{-3}$	$1.12 \cdot 10^{-3}$	g $\cdot$ coulomb^{-1}

*Here, and in the subsequent entries, we give the rest mass of the particle.

**In calculating mass defect and binding energy, the more accurate values for the mass of the elementary particles should be used.

INDEX

Absorbed dose, 143
  integral, 146
Absorbed dose rate, 146
Acceleration, 14, 87
Ampere (amp) unit, 88
  international, 88
Ampere, absolute, 88
Ampere-turn, 99, 100
Amplitude, 65
Angstrom (Å), 55, 133
Atmosphere (atm), standard (physical), 57
Atomic mass unit (amu), 56
Avogadro, 147
Avogadro's number, 160

Barye, 24
Bel (b), 64, 68
Biot-Savart, law, 114
Brightness, 141
British Thermal Unit (BTU), 72, 76

Candle, 139
Calorie, 72
  kilogram (kcal), 76
Capacitance, 92, 107
Cavendish, 11
Celsius (C) scale, 73
Cent, 70
Centigrade, 73
Centimeter (cm), 73
Charge, 88
  unit of, 103
Chemical mass unit (cmu), 56
Circuit, inductance of, 100
Conversion of units, 45
Coulomb (unit), 88
Coulomb's law, 95
Curie, 142
Current, 111
Cycle, 64

Decay constant, 142
Decibel (db), 64, 68
Degree, 72, 73, 76
Dielectric permittivity, 87, 94
Dimensional equation, 7
Dimensions, definition of, 7
  of units, 7

Dipole moment, 107
Dyne, 24, 29

Electric field, electric displacement of, 95
  intensity of, 93, 105
Electrodynamic constant, 126
Electromagnetic waves, sources of, 133
Electrostatic unit (esu), 102
Eman, 142
Energy, 36
Equivalent biological roentgen (EBR), 145
Erg, 24, 29

Fahrenheit (F) scale, 73
Farad, 92
Farad/meter, 94
Faraday-Maxwell, law, 100
Flux, electric induction, 96
  energy, intensity of, 136
  linkage of, 96
  luminous, 139
  magnetic, 96, 97
  mean sound energy, 66
  radiation energy, 135
  sound energy, 66
  spectral radiation energy, 135
Foot, 1, 31
Foot-poundal, 50
Force, 15, 87
  magnetic, 99
  moment of, 29, 36
Fuel, 77
Fundamental equation, definition of, 5
Fundamental quantities, 5
Fundamental units, 1, 5
Fusion, heat of, 80
Frequency, 64
  cyclic (angular), 21

Gauss, 5
General Conferences on Weights and Measures, 11
Giorgi, Giovanni, 13
Gram, 73
Gravitation constant, 10

Half-life, 142
Heat, 76

Heat capacity, 78
Heaviside, O., 122
Henry (unit), 100
Hopkinson's formula, 121
Horsepower (hp), 43

Inductance, 116
Inertia, moment of, 49
Integral energy density, 134
International Weights and Measures Office, 2

Joule (unit), 19

Kelvin (K) scale, 73
Kilocycle (kc), 64
Kilogram (kg), 14, 72
Kilojoule, 58

Length, 87
Linear expansion, coefficient of, 77
Liter (ℓ), 2, 55
Lorentz force, 118
Loudness, 69
Lumen, 139
Lux, 140

Mache, 143
Magnetic field, intensity of, 98
Magnetic induction, 97
Magnetic moment, 98
Magnetic permeability, 87, 101
Mass, 87
  magnetic, 99
Maxwell, 113
Mechanical units, 87
Megohm, 2
Meter, 72
  light standard, 13
Mev, 59
Micron (μ), definition of, 55
Millimicron (mμ), definition of, 55
Millioctave, 70
Molar heat capacity, 79
Momentum, 18
Multiple units, 1

Neper (nep), 64, 68
Newton (unit), 7, 16,
  law of gravitation, 10
  second law, 39
Nit, 141
Nonsystem units, 55

Octave, 70
Oersted, 112
Ohm, 2, 93
Ostrogradskiy-Gauss theorem, 120

Phon, 69
Phot, 140
Picofarad, 2
Pieza, 58
Pitch, 70
Plutonium, 147
Potential (voltage, emf), 89
Poundal, 33
Pound-force, 39
Pound-mass, 31
Prefixes for units, 2
Proportionality factor, 4, 9

Rad, 144
Radioactive concentration, 142
Radioactivity, 142
  decay, 142
Radiation, biological effect of, 145, 146
  α, β, γ, 141
  corpuscular, 143, 144
  electromagnetic, energy density of, 134
Rays, X and γ, 136
Réaumur (R) scale, 73, 74
Rep, 144
Resistance, 93, 108
Roentgen, 144
RPM, definition of, 56
RPS, definition of, 56
Rutherford (unit), 142

Savart (unit), 70
Second, definition of, 14, 72
Slug, 40
  metric, 25
Sound, 64
  energy density of, 65
  intensity level of, 67, 68
  pressure, 64
Source, candlepower of, 139
Specific activity, 143
Spectral energy density, 134, 135
Sten, 57
Steradian, 13
Stilb, 141
Stress, 33
Submultiple units, 1
Surface charge density, 89, 105
Surface tension coefficient, 82
System, absolute, 12
  British "absolute", 12
  British "gravitational", 12, 38
  cgs, of units, 13
  MKS, 6, 8
  MKGFS, 13
  MKSAr, 122
  practical, 12
Systems, magnetic and electrical, units of, 3, 12
  mechanical, units of, 12

Temperature, 73
  absolute zero, 160

Thermal conductivity, 83, 84
Threshold, audibility, 69
  feeling, 70
Thompson, 22
Torque, 15
Torque impulse, 15, 20

Unit of measurement, 1

Vaporization, heat of, 81
Velocity, 4, 14, 87

Viscosity, kinematic, coefficient of, 82
  dynamic coefficient of, 81
Visibility factor, 139
Volt (v), 89
Volumetric expansion, coefficient of, 78
Volumetric heat capacity, 79

Watt (unit), 19, 47
Weber (unit), 97
Weber–Fechner, law, 69